Assessment Resources

Grade 6

Glenda Lappan
James T. Fey
William M. Fitzgerald
Susan Friel
Elizabeth Difanis Phillips

PEARSON

Prentice
Hall

Boston, Massachusetts
Upper Saddle River, New Jersey

Connected Mathematics™ Project was developed at Michigan State University with financial support from the Michigan State University Office of the Provost, Computing and Technology, and the College of Natural Science.

Connected Mathematics™ is based upon work supported by the National Science Foundation under Grant No. MDR 9150217 and Grant No. ESI 9986372. Opinions expressed are those of the authors and not necessarily those of the Foundation.

The Michigan State University authors and administration have agreed that all MSU royalties arising from this publication will be devoted to purposes supported by the Department of Mathematics and the MSU Mathematics Enrichment Fund.

Acknowledgments The people who made up the *Connected Mathematics 2* team—representing editorial, editorial services, design services, and production services—are listed below. Bold type denotes core team members.

Leora Adler, Judith Buice, Kerry Cashman, Patrick Culleton, Sheila DeFazio, Katie Hallahan, Richard Heater, **Barbara Holllingdale, Jayne Holman,** Karen Holtzman, **Etta Jacobs,** Christine Lee, Carolyn Lock, Catherine Maglio, **Dotti Marshall,** Rich McMahon, Eve Melnechuk, Terri Mitchell, **Marsha Novak,** Irene Rubin, Donna Russo, Robin Samper, Siri Schwartzman, **Nancy Smith,** Emily Soltanoff, **Mark Tricca,** Paula Vergith, Roberta Warshaw, Helen Young.

ISBN 0-13-133977-X
2 3 4 5 6 7 8 9 10   09 08 07 06

Table of Contents

Check-Up 1

List all the factors of each number.

1. 24

2. 31

3. List all the proper factors of 35.

4. Which of the numbers in Questions 1–3 (24, 31, 35) are *prime* numbers? Explain why.

5. Which of the numbers in Questions 1–3 (24, 31, 35) are *composite* numbers? Explain why.

6. a. You are playing the Product Game on a game board like the one shown. One of the paper clips is on 7. What products can you make by moving the other paper clip?

b. List four multiples of 7 that are not on the game board.

7. Why isn't the number 13 on the Product Game board?

The Product Game

1	2	3	4	5
6	7	8	9	10
12	14	15	16	20
21	24	25	28	32
35	40	49	56	64

1 2 3 4 5 6 7 8

Check-Up 2

1. Which of these numbers are square numbers? Explain.

25   36   48

2. a. List the factors of 16 and the factors of 28.

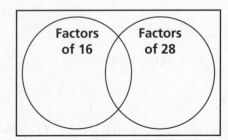

Factors of 16   Factors of 28

b. Complete the Venn diagram at the right.

c. What is the greatest common factor of 16 and 28?

3. a. List the first five multiples of 15 and the first five multiples of 12.

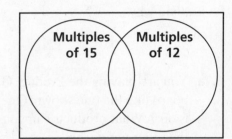

Multiples of 15   Multiples of 12

b. Complete the Venn diagram at the right.

c. What is the least common multiple of 15 and 12?

d. Find a common multiple of 15 and 12 that is not in your lists.

4. Jill says 6 is a common factor of 56 and 36. Is she correct? Explain your reasoning.

Partner Quiz

1. Evonne and Dolphus found a new Product Game board. Three of the factors and one of the products were not filled in.

4	6	8	9
12	16	18	24
27	32	36	48
54	64	72	▨

2　▨　▨　▨　8　9

   a. What are the other three factors you would need in order to play the game using this board?

   b. What product is missing?

2. Terrapin Crafts wants to rent between 35 and 40 square yards of space for a big crafts show. The space must be rectangular, and the side lengths must be whole numbers. Find the number(s) between 35 and 40 with the most factor pairs that give(s) the greatest number of rectangular arrangements to choose from.

Partner Quiz (continued)

3. Two radio stations are playing the #1 hit song "2 Nice 2 B True" by Anita and the Goody-2-Shoes. WMTH plays the song every 18 minutes. WMSU plays the song every 24 minutes. Both stations play the song at 3:00 P.M. When is the next time the stations will play the song at the same time?

4. Judith is planning a party for her younger brother. She has 36 prizes and 24 balloons. How many children can she have at the party so that each child gets an equal number of prizes and an equal number of balloons? Explain your answer.

Multiple-Choice Items

1. What is the greatest common factor of 16 and 28?

    A. 2   **B.** 3   **C.** 4   **D.** 112

2. Which number is a factor of 44?

    F. 8   **G.** 11   **H.** 14   **J.** 24

3. Which number is a multiple of 15?

    A. 1   **B.** 5   **C.** 10   **D.** 30

4. How many different factors does 20 have?

    F. 2   **G.** 3   **H.** 4   **J.** 6

5. Which number is a common multiple of 7 and 4?

    A. 11   **B.** 24   **C.** 48   **D.** 56

Multiple-Choice Items (continued)

6. What is the prime factorization of 160?

    F. $1 \times 2 \times 2 \times 2 \times 2 \times 2 \times 5$

    G. $2 \times 2 \times 2 \times 10$

    H. $2^4 \times 5$

    J. $2 \times 2 \times 2 \times 2 \times 2 \times 5$

7. What is the least common multiple of 18 and 28?

    A. 2   **B.** 9   **C.** 252   **D.** 504

8. Which answer is *always* odd?

    F. odd $\times$ odd   **G.** odd + odd   **H.** even $\times$ odd   **J.** even + even

9. Which string of factors is not a factorization of 180?

    A. $2 \times 3 \times 10 \times 3$

    B. $2^3 \times 3^2 \times 5$

    C. $2^2 \times 3 \times 3 \times 5$

    D. $2 \times 15 \times 6$

10. What is the least number that has 2, 3, and 4 as factors?

    F. 6   **G.** 9   **H.** 12   **J.** 18

Notebook Checklist

Place a ✓ next to each item you have completed.

Notebook Organization

_____ Problems and Mathematical Reflections are labeled and dated.

_____ Work is neat and easy to find and follow.

Vocabulary

_____ All words are listed.   _____ All words are defined or described.

Assessments

_____ Check-Up 1   _____ Partner Quiz

_____ Check-Up 2   _____ Unit Test

Assignments

_____ _____   _____ _____

_____ _____   _____ _____

_____ _____   _____ _____

_____ _____   _____ _____

_____ _____   _____ _____

_____ _____   _____ _____

_____ _____   _____ _____

_____ _____   _____ _____

_____ _____   _____ _____

_____ _____   _____ _____

_____ _____   _____ _____

_____ _____   _____ _____

_____ _____   _____ _____

_____ _____   _____ _____

_____ _____   _____ _____

Notebook Checklist

Self Assessment

Mathematical Ideas

After studying the mathematics in *Prime Time*:

1. a. I learned these things about numbers and their properties:

b. Here are page numbers of notebook entries that give evidence of what I have learned, along with descriptions of what each entry shows:

2. a. These are the mathematical ideas that I am still struggling with:

b. This is why I think these ideas are difficult for me:

c. Here are page numbers of notebook entries that give evidence of what I am struggling with, along with descriptions of what each entry shows:

Class Participation

I contributed to the classroom **discussion** and understanding of *Prime Time* when I . . . (Give examples.)

Self Assessment *(continued)*

Learning Environment

Rate each learning activity listed below using this scale:

1 I consistently struggled to understand the mathematics and I'm still not sure that I understand it.

2 I struggled somewhat but now I understand more than I did.

3 I had to work, but I feel confident that I understand now.

4 I understood everything pretty easily and I feel confident that I know the mathematics in these problems.

5 Everything came easily. I knew most of the mathematics before we did this.

Learning Activities:

_____ Problems from the Investigations

_____ ACE Homework Assignments

_____ Mathematical Reflections

_____ Check-Ups

_____ Partner Quiz

_____ Looking Back and Looking Ahead

_____ Unit Test

Check any of the following that you feel are the most helpful in adding to the success of your learning.

❑ Working on my own in class

❑ Discussing a problem with a partner

❑ Working in a small group of 3 or 4 people

❑ Discussing a problem as a whole class

❑ Individual or group presentation to the whole class

❑ Hearing how other people solved the problem

❑ Summarizing the mathematics as a class and taking notes

❑ Completing homework assignments

Unit Test

1. Find three different ways to show factorizations (strings of factors) of the number 16. Do not use 1 as a factor.

2. Find the prime factorization of the following two numbers. Show your work.

   a. 72   **b.** 132

3. A number that is less than 85 has 26 and 6 as factors. Find the number and explain your reasoning.

4. What number has the prime factorization $2^2 \times 3 \times 5^2 \times 7$? Show how you found the number.

5. Find the dimensions of all of the rectangles that can be made from 48 square tiles. Explain how you found your answers.

Unit Test *(continued)*

6. "Sam" and "Martha" are the local names for two lighthouses that guard a particularly dangerous part of the coast. Sam blinks every 12 seconds and Martha blinks every 8 seconds. They blink together at midnight. How many seconds will pass before they blink together again?

7. Carlos is packing sacks for treats at Halloween. Each sack has to have exactly the same stuff in it or the neighborhood kids complain. He has on hand 96 small candy bars and 64 small popcorn balls.

   a. What is the greatest number of treat sacks he can make?

   b. How many of each kind of treat is in one sack?

8. a. What is the greatest common factor of 30 and 42?

   b. Give a different common factor of 30 and 42.

   c. What is the least common multiple of 30 and 42?

   d. Give an additional common multiple of 30 and 42.

9. Dawson wrote the factorization $3^2 \times 5^2$. Without finding the actual number, how can Dawson tell if the number is even or odd?

Assign these questions as additional homework, or use them as review, quiz, or test questions.

1. Scarlett and Rhett were playing the Factor Game when Ashley looked over and saw that the numbers 1 to 15 were all circled. Ashley immediately said, "Oh, I see that your game is over." Is Ashley correct? Explain.

For Questions 2–4, describe how you can tell whether a given number is a multiple of the number shown.

2. 2   3. 3   4. 5

5. List all multiples of 6 between 1 and 100. What do these numbers have in common?

6. Mr. Matsumoto said, "I am thinking of a number. I know that to be sure I find all of the factor pairs of this number, I have to check all the numbers from 1 through 15."

   a. What is the smallest number he could be thinking of? Explain.

   b. What is the greatest number he could be thinking of? Explain.

7. What is the mystery number?
   Clue 1: My number is between the square numbers 1 and 25.
   Clue 2: My number has exactly two factors.
   Clue 3: Both 66 and 605 are multiples of my number.

8. Use concepts you have learned in this unit to make a mystery number question. Each clue must contain at least one word from your vocabulary list.

9. a. List the first ten square numbers.

   b. Give all the factors for each number you listed in part (a).

   c. Which of the square numbers you listed have only three factors?

   d. If you continued your list, what would be the next square number with only three factors?

10. A mystery number is greater than 50 and less than 100. You can make exactly five different rectangles with the mystery number of tiles. Its prime factorization consists of only one prime number. What is the number?

11. A number has 4 and 5 as factors.

    a. What other numbers must be factors? Explain.

    b. What is the smallest the number could be?

12. Chairs for a meeting are arranged in six rows. Each row has the same number of chairs.

   a. What is the minimum possible number of chairs that could be in the room?

   b. Suppose 100 is the maximum number of chairs allowed in the meeting room. What other numbers of chairs are possible?

13. Gloomy Toothpaste comes in two sizes: 9 ounces for $0.89 and 12 ounces for $1.15.

   a. Ben and Aaron bought the same amount of toothpaste. Ben bought only 9-ounce tubes, and Aaron bought only 12-ounce tubes. What is the smallest possible number of tubes each boy bought? (*Hint:* Use your knowledge of multiples to help you.)

   b. Which size tube is the better buy?

14. Circle the letter(s) of the statements that are always *true* about any prime number.

   a. It is divisible by only itself and 1.

   b. It is a factor of 1.

   c. It is divisible by another prime number.

   d. It is always an odd number.

15. Tyrone claims that the longest string of factors for 48 is $48 = 2 \times 2 \times 2 \times 2 \times 3$. Ian says there is a longer string. He wrote $48 = 1 \times 1 \times 1 \times 1 \times 1 \times 2 \times 2 \times 2 \times 2 \times 3$. Who is correct? Why?

16. What is the smallest number divisible by the first three prime numbers and the first three composite numbers? Explain.

17. Suppose you are playing the Factor Game on the 30-board. Your opponent goes first and chooses 29, giving you only 1 point. It is now your turn to choose a number. Which number would be your best move? Why?

18. Suppose the person who sits next to you was absent the day you played the Factor Game. On the back of this paper, write a note to him or her explaining the strategies you have discovered for winning the Factor Game. Include a description of how you decide which move to make when it is your turn.

19. Vicente made three dozen cookies for the student council bake sale. He wants to package them in small bags with the same number of cookies in each bag.

   a. List all the ways Vicente can package the cookies.

   b. If you were Vicente, how many cookies would you put in each bag? Why?

   c. Vicente spent $5.40 on ingredients for the cookies. The student council will pay him back for the money he spent. For each of the answers in part (a), determine how much the student council should charge for each bag of cookies so they make a profit yet still get students to buy the cookies.

20. Marcia has developed a rule for generating a number sequence. The first six numbers in her sequence are 7, 21, 42, 126, 252, 756.

   a. What is Marcia's rule for finding the numbers in her sequence? Explain.

   b. What are the next two numbers in Marcia's sequence?

   c. What is the greatest common factor (GCF) of all the terms in Marcia's sequence? Explain your reasoning.

21. a. List two pairs of numbers whose least common multiple (LCM) is the same as their product. For example, the least common multiple of 5 and 6 is 30 and $5 \times 6 = 30$.

   b. List two pairs of numbers whose least common multiple is smaller than their product. For example, the least common multiple of 6 and 9 is 18 and 18 is less than 6×9.

   c. For a given pair of numbers, how can you tell whether the least common multiple will be less than or equal to their product?

22. a. Write the prime factorization of 900.

   b. From information in the prime factorization of 900, write five sentences about the number 900. Use vocabulary from the unit in each sentence.

Partner Quiz A

1. Trey's car has a 20-gallon gas tank. The gas gauge right now looks like the one shown. Suppose Trey buys 10 gallons of gas. What will be the new reading on the gas gauge?

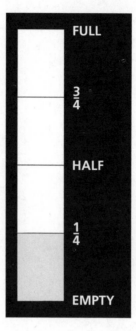

2. The drawing below shows part of an inch ruler. **The picture has been enlarged.** Each inch is broken into smaller pieces to measure more accurately than in whole inches. Label each mark on the ruler with a correct fraction.

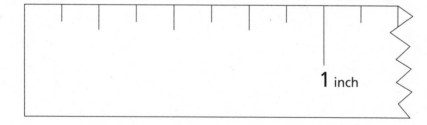

Partner Quiz A *(continued)*

3. Julie and Don's math classes are selling sub sandwiches as a fundraiser. Julie's class has reached $\frac{2}{3}$ of their goal and Don's class has reached $\frac{3}{4}$ of their goal. Julie says her class has collected more money than Don's class.

   a. Mark and label the thermometers to show how Julie could be right. Explain your reasoning.

Goal ⌐   Goal ⌐

Julie   **Don**

   b. Mark and label the thermometers to show how Julie could be wrong. Explain your reasoning.

Goal ⌐   Goal ⌐

Julie   **Don**

Check-Up

1. Compare the fractions in each pair. Insert the correct sign: <, >, or =. Explain your reasoning.

   a. $\frac{2}{4}$ $\frac{7}{12}$

                                       b. $\frac{5}{8}$ $\frac{6}{10}$

   c. $\frac{8}{12}$ $\frac{10}{15}$

                                       d. $\frac{3}{8}$ $\frac{3}{12}$

2. Name three different fractions between $\frac{1}{2}$ and $\frac{3}{4}$.

3. The diagram represents $\frac{1}{5}$ of a fifths fraction strip. Sketch the whole strip.

4. Order these numbers from least to greatest: $1\frac{3}{4}$ $\frac{8}{3}$ $\frac{19}{10}$

Partner Quiz B

1. On the strip below, mark and label the location of each decimal:

0.09   0.9   0.19   0.190   0.019

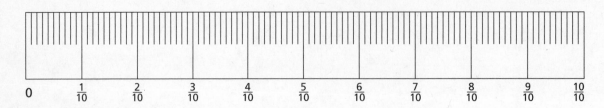

2. Drevon had to find four fractions less than $\frac{3}{4}$. He wrote the following on his paper. Circle the correct statements and show why they are correct.

$$\frac{7}{8} < \frac{3}{4} \qquad\qquad \frac{2}{3} < \frac{3}{4} \qquad\qquad \frac{65}{100} < \frac{3}{4} \qquad\qquad \frac{14}{20} < \frac{3}{4}$$

3. Find three numbers between 0.47 and 0.48

Partner Quiz B *(continued)*

4. Parker Middle School ordered 121 boxes of markers. If there are 22 teachers, how many boxes does each teacher get? Write your answer as a fraction and as a decimal.

5. Fill in the missing decimal numbers on this number line:

SAMPLE

0.19   0.23

Answer:

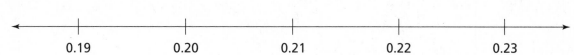

0.19   0.20   0.21   0.22   0.23

For each number line, fill in the missing decimal numbers.

a.

0.28   0.34

b.

0.36   0.37

Multiple-Choice Items

1. Wilson Middle School has ten sixth-grade classes. Two of the classes have both band and chorus. What percent of the sixth-grade classes have both band and chorus?

   A. 2%   **B.** 10%   **C.** 20%   **D.** 40%

2. What percent of the grid is shaded?

   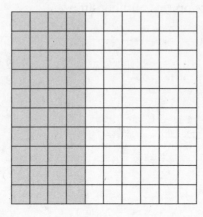

   F. 4%   **G.** 40%   **H.** 60%   **J.** $66\frac{2}{3}$%

3. What decimal is equal to $\frac{3}{5}$?

   A. 0.06   **B.** 0.30   **C.** 0.35   **D.** 0.60

4. How would you write $1\frac{1}{10}$ as a percent?

   F. 110%   **G.** 11%   **H.** 100%   **J.** 1.10%

5. Which figure has the smallest fraction of area shaded?

   A.    **B.**   **C.** 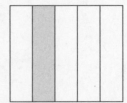   **D.**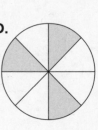

Multiple-Choice Items (continued)

6. There are 30 students doing an experiment in science class. If 40% of the students are measuring the chemicals for an experiment, what percent are not measuring chemicals?

    F. 12%   **G.** 18%   **H.** 40%   **J.** 60%

7. How would you write $8\frac{2}{3}$ as an improper fraction?

    A. $\frac{13}{3}$ **B.** $\frac{26}{3}$ **C.** $\frac{22}{3}$ **D.** $\frac{24}{3}$

8. Which fraction is not equivalent to $\frac{12}{20}$?

    F. $\frac{36}{60}$ **G.** $\frac{3}{4}$ **H.** $\frac{6}{10}$ **J.** $\frac{9}{15}$

9. Which of the following is equivalent to $\frac{4}{5}$?

    A. $\frac{45}{100}$ **B.** $\frac{5}{6}$ **C.** $\frac{40}{50}$ **D.** $\frac{3}{4}$

10. Which of the following is equivalent to $\frac{9}{4}$?

    F. 2.25   **G.** 0.94   **H.** 9.4   **J.** 1.25

Notebook Checklist

Place a ✓ next to each item you have completed.

Notebook Organization

_____ Problems and Mathematical Reflections are labeled and dated.

_____ Work is neat and easy to find and follow.

Vocabulary

_____ All words are listed.   _____ All words are defined or described.

Assessments

_____ Partner Quiz A   _____ Partner Quiz B

_____ Check-Up   _____ Unit Test

Assignments

_____ _____   _____ _____

_____ _____   _____ _____

_____ _____   _____ _____

_____ _____   _____ _____

_____ _____   _____ _____

_____ _____   _____ _____

_____ _____   _____ _____

_____ _____   _____ _____

_____ _____   _____ _____

_____ _____   _____ _____

_____ _____   _____ _____

_____ _____   _____ _____

_____ _____   _____ _____

_____ _____   _____ _____

Self Assessment

Mathematical Ideas

After studying the mathematics in *Bits and Pieces I*:

1. **a.** I learned these things about fractions, decimals, and percents:

   b. Here are page numbers of notebook entries that give evidence of what I have learned, along with descriptions of what each entry shows:

2. **a.** These are the mathematical ideas that I am still struggling with:

   b. This is why I think these ideas are difficult for me:

   c. Here are page numbers of notebook entries that give evidence of what I am struggling with, along with descriptions of what each entry shows:

Class Participation

I contributed to the classroom **discussion** and understanding of *Bits and Pieces I* when I . . . (Give examples.)

Self Assessment (continued)

Learning Environment

Rate each learning activity listed below using this scale:

1   I consistently struggled to understand the mathematics and I'm still not sure that I understand it.

2   I struggled somewhat but now I understand more than I did.

3   I had to work, but I feel confident that I understand now.

4   I understood everything pretty easily and I feel confident that I know the mathematics in these problems.

5   Everything came easily. I knew most of the mathematics before we did this.

Learning Activities:

_____ Problems from the Investigations

_____ ACE Homework Assignments

_____ Mathematical Reflections

_____ Check-Up

_____ Quizzes

_____ Looking Back and Looking Ahead

_____ Unit Test

Check any of the following that you feel are the most helpful in adding to the success of your learning.

❏   Working on my own in class.

❏   Discussing a problem with a partner.

❏   Working in a small group of 3 or 4 people.

❏   Discussing a problem as a whole class.

❏   Individual or group presentation to the whole class.

❏   Hearing how other people solved the problem.

❏   Summarizing the mathematics as a class and taking notes.

❏   Completing homework assignments.

Unit Test: In-Class Portion

1. Write each of the following as a fraction, decimal, and percent.

Words	Fraction	Decimal	Percent
a. 30 days out of 100 days			
b. 20 correct out of 25 problems			
c. 3 out of 4 games won			
d. 21 out of 40 mountain bikes			

2. There are 28 students in a math class, 16 of which are male.

   a. What fraction of the class is male? What percent is male?

   b. What fraction of the class is female? What percent is female?

3. For parts (a)–(c), circle the fraction, decimal or percent that is not equivalent to the others. Explain why it is not equivalent.

   a. 0.60   0.6   6%

   b. $\frac{1}{25}$ 25%   0.25

   c. $\frac{9}{5}$ 1.8   108%

Unit Test: In-Class Portion *(continued)*

4. This drawing shows part of a centimeter ruler and a paper clip. **The drawing has been enlarged.** The small marks indicate millimeters. The large marks indicate centimeters.

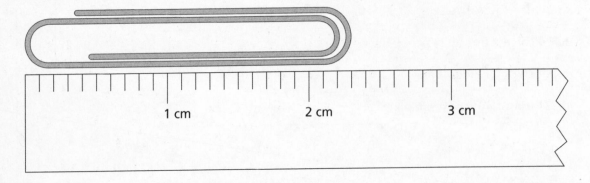

a. What fraction of a centimeter is each millimeter?

b. Show a mark on the ruler at 3.2 cm.

c. How many millimeters is 3.2 cm?

d. According to the ruler, how long is the paper clip?

5. Arrange these decimals from smallest to largest:

6.00   0.56   0.060   0.6   0.056

6. Blake was listening to his favorite radio station. He noticed that in one hour 15 songs were played and 3 of them were by the group from Michigan, RU Cold2. What percentage of the songs in that hour were by RU Cold2?

7. For each pair of fractions, decide if they are equivalent or not equivalent. Explain.

a. $\frac{3}{4} \overset{?}{=} \frac{10}{12}$ **b.** $\frac{5}{10} \overset{?}{=} \frac{4}{8}$ **c.** $\frac{10}{8} \overset{?}{=} 1\frac{1}{4}$

Unit Test In-Class Portion (continued)

8. **a.** How many thirds are in $3\frac{2}{3}$?

b. How many fourths are in $\frac{17}{4}$?

c. How many fifths are in 1.8?

9. For the figure below, give the fraction and decimal name for the shaded part.

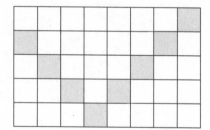

10. Write each fraction as a decimal.

   a. $2\frac{7}{100}$ **b.** $\frac{7}{8}$ **c.** $\frac{21}{30}$

11. Write each decimal number in words.

   a. 0.8   **b.** 0.04   **c.** 2.505

12. Write each decimal as a fraction.

   a. 0.8   **b.** 0.04   **c.** 2.505

Unit Test: Individual Research

Find two different articles in newspapers or magazines that contain fractions, decimals, or percents. If one article uses mainly one of these forms, the other article must contain at least one of the other two forms.

Write a one- to two-paragraph summary of each article. In your explanations, tell how the fractions, decimals, or percents are used in the article and what they represent. Attach your articles to your explanations.

Question Bank

Assign these questions as additional homework, or use them as review, quiz, or test questions.

1. The carnival game shown at the right tests strength. A player hits the block with a mallet and the force of the blow sends a metal ringer up the pole. If the player uses enough force, the ringer rings the bell at the top of the pole and the player receives the top prize of 100 points. The player receives fewer points for hits that only send the metal ringer part way up the pole. The points can be traded for tickets to rides at the carnival.

   a. Where should marks be made on the pole for each of the game point amounts? Mark them on the pole.

   10 points   25 points   35 points   70 points   85 points   100 points

   b. What fraction of the pole would each of the marks in part (a) represent?

   c. What payoff, in game points, should be given for sending the metal ringer $\frac{1}{3}$ of the way up the pole?

   d. What payoff, in game points, should be given for sending the ringer $\frac{3}{5}$ of the way up the pole?

   e. What payoff, in game points, should be given for sending the ringer $\frac{2}{8}$ of the way up the pole?

   f. What payoff, in game points, should be given for sending the ringer $\frac{3}{4}$ of the way up the pole?

   g. Miki's hit sent the metal ringer $\frac{5}{8}$ of the way up the pole. Taylor's hit went $\frac{6}{9}$ of the way to the top. Who received the most game points? Why?

2. You are invited to go out for pizza with several friends. When you get there, your friends are sitting in two separate groups. You can join either group. If you join the first group, there will be a total of 4 people in the group and you will be sharing 6 small pizzas.

   If you join the second group, there will be a total of 6 people in the group and you will be sharing 8 small pizzas. If pizza will be shared equally in each group, and you are *very* hungry, which group would you rather join? Explain your choice.

3. a. Three is what fractional part of 12?

   b. Five is what fractional part of 20?

   c. Two is what fractional part of 9?

   d. Seven is what fractional part of 17?

4. Samuel is getting a snack for himself and his little brother. There are two muffins in the refrigerator. Samuel takes half of one muffin for himself and half of the other muffin for his little brother. His little brother complains that Samuel got more. Samuel says that he got $\frac{1}{2}$ and his brother got $\frac{1}{2}$. What might be the problem?

5. Your best friend was absent when your class learned how to compare decimal numbers. Write a set of directions that would help your friend understand how to compare decimal numbers.

6. The following prices were posted at a local store.

Bananas: .39¢ a pound

Notebook Paper: 1.02¢

What is wrong with these signs?

7. Use these numbers to fill in the blanks so that the story makes numerical sense:

645    $\frac{3}{4}$ 65   215   75   161.25   35 $\frac{1}{4}$ 330.65

Events Night a Huge Success!

The Events Night held by Mr. Martinez's and Ms. Swanson's middle-school classes was a success, raising a total of $ _____. The teachers estimated the large turnout of middle-school students included over _____ of the building's student population. Over half of the money, $ _____, was earned by the food booths. _____ game tickets were sold, raising $ _____ which represented _____ of the money. The tickets were _____ cents each. Most of the money that was raised (_____ %) will go toward paying for the class camping trip, and the other _____ % will be used to pay expenses.

8. Use your fraction strips or another method to compare the two fractions in each pair. Insert the correct sign: $<$, $>$, or $=$.

a. $\frac{8}{12}$ $\frac{3}{4}$ **b.** $\frac{5}{8}$ $\frac{6}{10}$ **c.** $\frac{2}{3}$ $\frac{5}{6}$ **d.** $\frac{2}{4}$ $\frac{7}{12}$ **e.** $\frac{3}{8}$ $\frac{3}{12}$

9. This sketch shows part of a ruler. The main marks indicate inches.

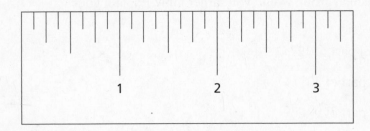

How should each of the marks between the inches be labeled? Explain.

10. Write a benchmark fraction that is close to each of these percentages:

    a. 23.6%
                    b. 45.4545%

11. Order these numbers from least to greatest:

$$1\frac{7}{10} \qquad 1\frac{15}{18} \qquad \frac{24}{15}$$

12. Give a fraction name for the shaded part of the figure below. Explain how you figured out what fractional part of the whole was shaded.

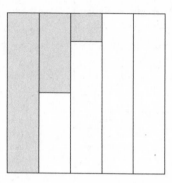

13. Lynette found a worm that is $\frac{2}{3}$ of the length of a fraction strip. How many worms exactly like hers would you need to put end to end that equal two times the length of the fraction strip? Explain your answer.

14. Decide whether each of the following statements is true or false. Explain.

    a. If you compare two fractions with the same denominator, the fraction with the greater numerator is greater.

    b. If you compare two fractions with the same numerator, the fraction with the greater denominator is greater.

15. Antonio's father has a cutting form that can cut a pizza into 12 slices and another form that can cut a pizza into 8 slices.

    a. If a family bought three small slices and three large slices, what fraction of a pizza did they buy? (You might want to draw a picture to help you.)

    b. How much more pizza (as a fraction) would they need to buy to purchase a whole pizza?

    c. How many different ways can you combine small slices and large slices to make a whole pizza? Write each of your responses as number sentences.

    SAMPLE

    $\frac{2}{8} + \frac{9}{12} = 1$ means that two large slices and nine small slices will make one whole pizza.

16. On each figure below, shade the indicated decimal amount.

a. 0.375

b. 0.6

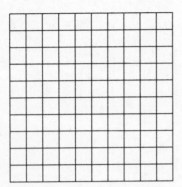 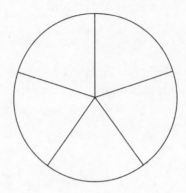

c. 0.05

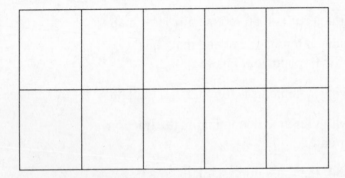

17. In each figure, express the area shaded and the area not shaded as percents.

a.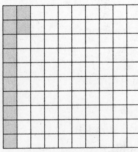

shaded:
not shaded:

b.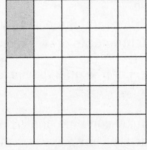

shaded:
not shaded:

c.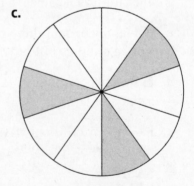

shaded:
not shaded:

18. In a recent survey of 600 people, 20% said chocolate chip cookie was their favorite ice cream. How many people in the survey favored chocolate chip cookie ice cream? Explain your answer.

19. Rename each of the decimal amounts as a fraction.

    a. 0.375   **b.** 0.6   **c.** 0.05

20. For each number line, fill in the missing decimal numbers.

SAMPLE

Answer:

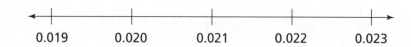

a.

b.

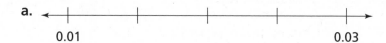

c.

21. In each pair of pencils, the length of the new pencil is about what fraction of the length of the old pencil?

a.

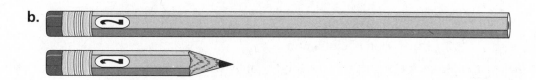

b.

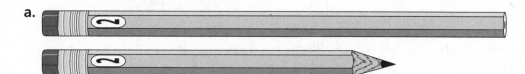

22. Estimate and mark where the number 1 will be on each number line. The length that represents the whole may be different on each number line.

a.

0    $\frac{1}{6}$

b.

0    $\frac{3}{4}$

c.

0    $\frac{3}{2}$

23. a. In the drawing below, what part of the unsharpened pencil is the sharpened pencil? Express your answer as a fraction and a decimal.

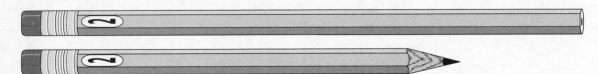

b. What part of the sharpened pencil is the unsharpened pencil? Express your answer as a fraction and a decimal.

24. The average human body temperature is 98.6° (98 and $\frac{6}{10}$)° Fahrenheit. For parts (a)–(c), tell whether the thermometer shows this temperature.

a.

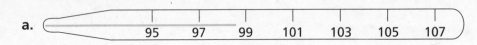

95   97   99   101   103   105   107

b.

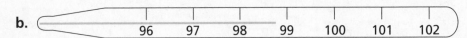

96   97   98   99   100   101   102

c.

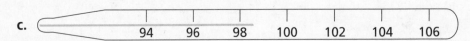

94   96   98   100   102   104   106

25. Michael decided to make French toast for himself and his other four family members. He finds a recipe that calls for:

8 slices of bread

4 eggs

1 cup of milk

1 teaspoon of cinnamon

a. If he makes a single recipe and shares the food equally with his family, how much French toast will each person receive?

b. How much egg will each person have in their French toast?

Check-Up

1. Describe all the symmetries in the following polygon. Explain.

2. Use shapes A, B, C, D, E, or F from your Shapes Set to answer parts (a)–(b).

    a. Choose one shape and show that it tiles.

    b. Choose one shape and show that it does not tile.

Check-Up (continued)

3. a. Use an angle ruler to draw a 100° angle.

   b. Use an angle ruler to measure the following angle.

4. One of the most common places we see angles is on the faces of clocks. At the start of each hour, the minute hand is pointed straight up, at the 12. Without using an angle ruler, find the measure of the following angle.

Partner Quiz

1. a. Can a square be used to tile a floor? Explain why or why not.

b. Can a regular pentagon be used to tile a floor? Explain why or why not.

2. In the figure below, lines *TU* and *VW* are parallel. The measure of angle 3 is 40°. Find the measures of angles 1, 5, and 6.

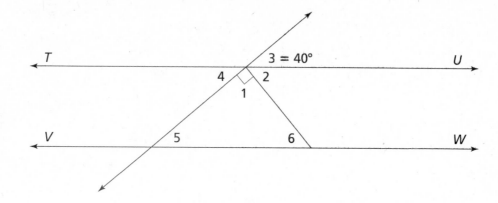

a. measure of angle 1 = _____ Explain:

b. measure of angle 5 = _____ Explain:

c. measure of angle 6 = _____ Explain:

3. Is it possible for a parallelogram to have a 54° angle and a 126° angle? Explain why or why not.

4. The diagram below is a regular hexagon. Find the measure of the angle marked *x*.

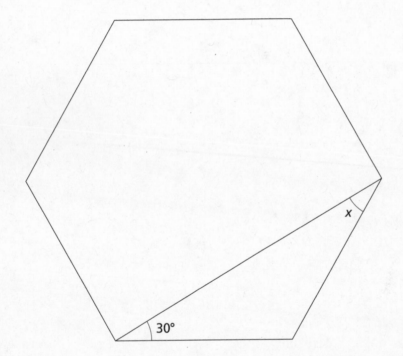

Name _____ Date _____ Class _____

Multiple-Choice Items

1. Polygon *ABCD* is a rectangle and the lengths of *AD* and *DE* are equal. What is the measure of angle *BAE*?

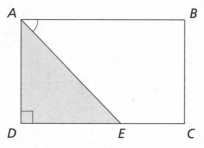

   A. 90°   **B.** 40°   **C.** 45°   **D.** 100°

2. The figure below is a regular pentagon. Which expression represents the perimeter (distance around) the pentagon?

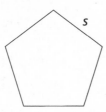

   F. $5 \times s$ **G.** $s + 5$ **H.** $s + s + s + s$ **J.** $s \times s$

3. Which figure below is a polygon?

 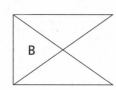 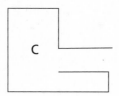 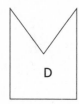

   A. Figure A   **B.** Figure B   **C.** Figure C   **D.** Figure D

Multiple-Choice Items (continued)

4. In which figure is angle *DEF* less than 90°?

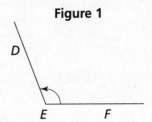

Figure 1

Figure 2

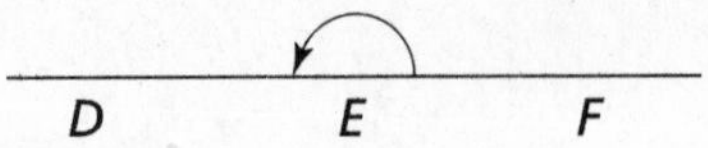

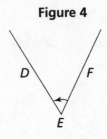

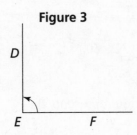

Figure 3

Figure 4

    F. Figure 1   **G.** Figure 2   **H.** Figure 3   **J.** Figure 4

5. Which of these drawings shows line *AB* parallel to line *CD* and line *CD* perpendicular to line *EF*?

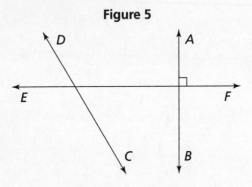

Figure 5

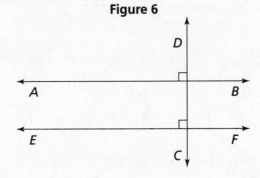

Figure 6

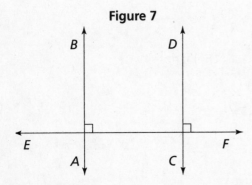

Figure 7

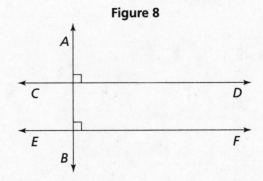

Figure 8

    A. Figure 5   **B.** Figure 6   **C.** Figure 7   **D.** Figure 8

Multiple-Choice Items *(continued)*

6. Name the polygon below.

    F. quadrilateral   **G.** hexagon   **H.** pentagon   **J.** octagon

7. Which is not a name for this polygon?

    A. quadrilateral   **B.** parallelogram

    C. rectangle   **D.** rhombus

8. What is the measure of the angle labeled *x*?

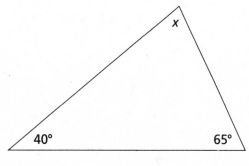

    F. 65°   **G.** 90°   **H.** 255°   **J.** 75°

Multiple-Choice Items *(continued)*

Notebook Checklist

Place a ✓ next to each item you have completed.

Notebook Organization

_____ Problems and Mathematical Reflections are labeled and dated.

_____ Work is neat and easy to find and follow.

Vocabulary

_____ All words are listed.

_____ All words are defined or described.

Assessments

_____ Check-Up

_____ Partner Quiz

_____ Unit Test

Assignments

_____ _____   _____ _____

_____ _____   _____ _____

_____ _____   _____ _____

_____ _____   _____ _____

_____ _____   _____ _____

_____ _____   _____ _____

_____ _____   _____ _____

_____ _____   _____ _____

_____ _____   _____ _____

_____ _____   _____ _____

_____ _____   _____ _____

_____ _____   _____ _____

Self Assessment

Mathematical Ideas

After studying the mathematics in *Shapes and Designs*:

1. a. I learned these things about how sides and angles form the shapes of polygons.

   b. Here are page numbers of notebook entries that give evidence of what I have learned, along with descriptions of what each entry shows:

2. a. These are the mathematical ideas that I am still struggling with:

   b. This is why I think these ideas are difficult for me:

   c. Here are page numbers of notebook entries that give evidence of what I am struggling with, along with descriptions of what each entry shows:

Class Participation

I contributed to the classroom **discussion** and understanding of *Shapes and Designs* when I . . . (Give examples.)

Self Assessment (continued)

Learning Environment

Rate each learning activity listed below using this scale:

1   I consistently struggled to understand the mathematics and I'm still not sure that I understand it.

2   I struggled somewhat but now I understand more than I did.

3   I had to work, but I feel confident that I understand now.

4   I understood everything pretty easily and I feel confident that I know the mathematics in these problems.

5   Everything came easily. I knew most of the mathematics before we did this.

Learning Activities:

_____ Problems from the Investigations

_____ ACE Homework Assignments

_____ Mathematical Reflections

_____ Check-Ups

_____ Quiz

_____ Unit Test

Check any of the following that you feel are the most helpful in adding to the success of your learning.

❑   Working on my own in class

❑   Discussing a problem with a partner

❑   Working in a small group of 3 or 4 people

❑   Discussing a problem as a whole class

❑   Individual or group presentation to the whole class

❑   Hearing how other people solved the problem

❑   Summarizing the mathematics as a class and taking notes

❑   Completing homework assignments

Unit Test

1. For the following polygon:

    a. Draw in the lines of symmetry.

    b. Describe the rotation symmetries.

2. a. What is the interior angle sum of a regular pentagon? Explain.

    b. How many degrees are in one exterior angle of a regular pentagon?

Unit Test (continued)

3. A triangle has side lengths measuring 3 and 7. The measurement of the longest side is missing. Ted says that one possibility for the unknown side length is 11. Do you agree with Ted? Explain why or why not.

4. Is it possible for a triangle to have angles with measures 34°, 45°, and 100°? Explain why or why not.

5. Is it possible to make two different quadrilaterals that both have side lengths 7, 7, 9, 9? Explain. (You may want to draw a picture.)

6. In the diagram below, estimate the measures of each numbered angle.

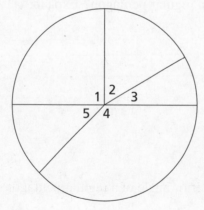

Unit Test (continued)

7. The diagram below shows rectangle *ABCD* with diagonal *CA*. Find the measure of the angle marked *x*.

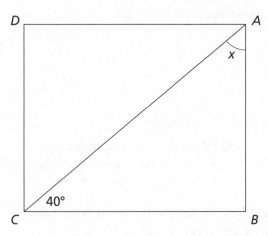

8. In the quadrilateral below, the top and bottom sides are parallel. Use the quadrilateral to answer parts (a)–(b).

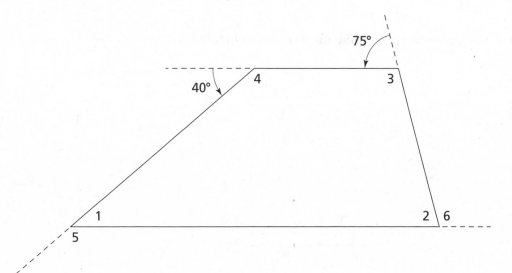

a. Find the measures of angles 1, 2, 3, and 4. Explain your answers.

b. Find the measure of angles 5 and 6.

Question Bank

Assign these questions as additional homework, or use them as review, quiz, or test questions.

1. Spread your fingers and look at the angles made by them. For parts (a)–(c), use your angle ruler to measure the angles formed by the given fingers. (To take the measure, lay your hand flat on your desk and spread the fingers you are measuring as far as possible.)

    a. your thumb and first finger

    b. your index and middle finger

    c. your thumb and pinkie finger

    d. How do your measurements for parts (a)–(c) compare?

2. Naomi wants measurements of 3, 6, 6, and 12 for the side lengths of a quadrilateral. Marcelo says he cannot make a quadrilateral with these lengths. Is he right? Explain.

For Questions 3–5, decide whether the given statement is true or false. Give explanations or sketches to support your answers.

3. A quadrilateral with sides 5, 8, 5, 8, in that order, is always a rectangle.

4. A quadrilateral with two sides of 7 and two sides of 11 is always a parallelogram.

5. You will always be able to draw two different triangles using side lengths of 3, 4, and 5.

For Questions 6–8, use a coordinate grid like the one shown below.

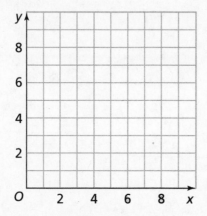

6. If a line segment connecting (4, 6) and (7, 6) forms one side of a square, what might be the coordinates of the other corners of the square?

7. If (2, 0) and (5, 5) are two vertices of a triangle that does not have a right angle, what might be the coordinates of the other vertex of the triangle?

8. Draw your triangle for Question 7. For each angle of the triangle, tell whether the angles are greater than or less than 90°.

9. Alejandro's dad bought regular-pentagon tiles to tile his patio. When he returned with the tiles and showed them to Alejandro, Alejandro told him that he would have to go back for another shape tile to go with the pentagon tiles or exchange the pentagon tiles for a different shape altogether. The pentagon alone would not work to tile the patio. Was Alejandro correct? Why or why not?

10. G. Oni O'Meter is a math rap singer who lives in Miami, Florida. She is starting a fall concert tour, and she flies her own plane to every concert. Here is her tour schedule:

City	Dates
Dallas, Texas	September 14–16
Boston, Massachusetts	September 18–20
San Diego, California	September 22–25
Detroit, Michigan	September 27–30
Miami, Florida	October 2–8

To fly from one city to the next, G. Oni needs a flight angle and compass direction to direct her plane. A flight angle is formed by two lines that start in the city from which the flight takes off. One line points north, and the other points to the flight's destination. The flight angles are labeled with degree measure and west or east.

For example, to fly from Miami to Dallas for the first concert, G. Oni flies along a 71° west flight angle. Using your angle ruler and the map below, find the flight angles for the rest of G. Oni's concert tour.

11. In the diagram, line L_1 is parallel to line L_2.

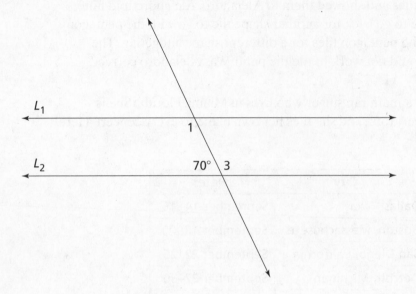

   a. What is the measure of angle 3? Explain.
   b. What is the measure of angle 1? Explain.

For Questions 12–19, decide whether the given statement is true or false. Give explanations or sketches to support your answers.

12. With side lengths measuring 6, 8, and 10, there is one and only one triangle shape that can be made.

13. Any two quadrilaterals that have sides of the same lengths will be identical in size and shape.

SAMPLE
Two quadrilaterals with side lengths measuring 5, 7, 9, and 11 will be the same size and shape.

14. All rectangles are special kinds of parallelograms.

15. All parallelograms are special kinds of squares.

16. You can always completely surround a point by placing the vertices of four squares together.

17. The sum of the measures of the angles of any triangle is 90°.

18. In a regular hexagon, all sides are the same length and all angles are 100°.

19. Any triangle can be used to tile a flat surface.

Use an angle ruler to measure each angle.

20.

21.

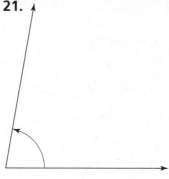

22.

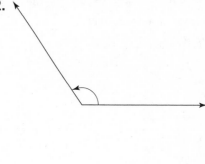

23. Draw a 90° angle.

24. Draw a 150° angle.

One of the most common places we see angles is on the faces of clocks. At the start of each hour, the minute hand is pointed straight up, at the 12. On the clocks below, mark where the minute hand is at the start of an hour as one side of an angle. Sketch the angle formed by the minute hand at the time shown, and give the measure of the angle.

25. 45 minutes

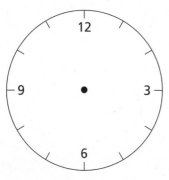

angle =

26. 25 minutes

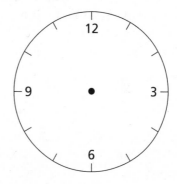

angle =

For each figure, use the given shape and measurements to find the lengths and angle measurements of all sides and angles in each figure. *Note:* Figures not shown at actual size.

27. square

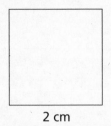

2 cm

28. rectangle

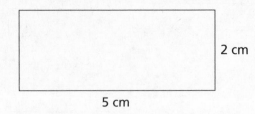

2 cm

5 cm

29. parallelogram

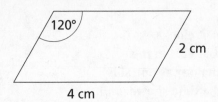

120°

2 cm

4 cm

30. parallelogram

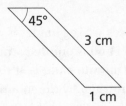

45°

3 cm

1 cm

31. Below is the face of a compass. You can match each compass direction with the degree measure of the angle formed by a clockwise turn from due north (N) to the desired direction. For example, east (E) has the direction number 90°.

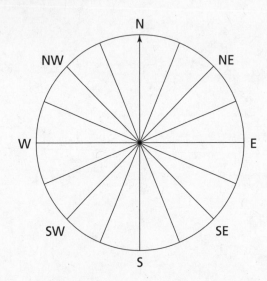

Find the direction number for the given point of the compass.

a. NE (northeast)
b. SE (southeast)
c. S (south)
d. SW (southwest)
e. W (west)
f. NW (northwest)
g. N (north)
h. NNE (north-northeast, between N and NE)

32. For parts (a)–(b), show all the line symmetries and give the degree measures for all the turn symmetries for the given shape.

a.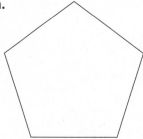

b.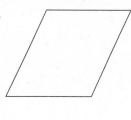

33. Jack has made a tiling with quadrilateral shapes. He can pick up a shape from his tiling, turn it 90°, and it will fit back where it was. Kenesha has used a different quadrilateral to make a tiling. Kenesha's quadrilateral will not fit back into the pattern when she turns it 90°.

   a. What might Jack's quadrilateral look like? Draw or describe it, and explain why it fits.

   b. What might Kenesha's quadrilateral look like? Draw or describe it, and explain why it doesn't fit back into the tiling pattern when it is turned 90°.

34. a. Is the triangle a regular polygon?
   Explain why or why not.

   b. Could this triangle be used to tile a surface?
   Explain why or why not.

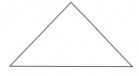

35. An equilateral triangle has a perimeter of 12. What is the length of each side? Explain.

36. A square has a perimeter of 16.4 centimeters. What is the length of each side? Explain.

37. For each of the shapes below, find the unknown angle measure without using your angle ruler.

a.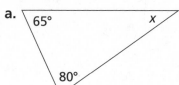

b.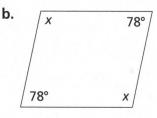

c.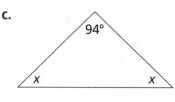

For Questions 38–41, use these shapes.

38. The figures I, L, and V can be grouped together, but X would not belong in the group. Explain.

39. The figures E, G, H, I, and M can be grouped together, but S would not belong in the group. Explain.

40. The figures F, Q, W, and X can be grouped together, but N would not belong in the group. Explain.

41. The figures A, B, H, J, M, S, and U can be grouped together, but N would not belong in the group. Explain.

Check-Up

1. Decide if each sum is closest to $0, \frac{1}{2}$, or 1. Explain your reasoning.

   a. $\frac{1}{4} + \frac{2}{3}$ **b.** $0.5 + \frac{1}{6}$ **c.** $\frac{1}{8} + \frac{3}{4}$

2. Which sum is closest to 1? Explain your reasoning.

   A. $0.5 + \frac{3}{4}$ **B.** $\frac{5}{6} + \frac{1}{4}$ **C.** $\frac{3}{4} + \frac{2}{3}$

3. At D. J.'s Drink Stand, Erika ordered a cup of fruit punch made with the following recipe.

   $\frac{1}{4}$ cup lemonade

   $\frac{1}{12}$ cup cranberry juice

   ▨ cup orange juice

   What fraction of Erika's cup will be orange juice? Write a number sentence to support your answer.

Check-Up *(continued)*

4. Mr. Gomez took some of his cross-country team out for pizza the night before a big race. He ordered three medium pizzas. They ate the following amounts:

$$\text{Scott ate } \tfrac{2}{3} \text{ of a pizza.}$$

$$\text{Nate ate } \tfrac{7}{12} \text{ of a pizza.}$$

$$\text{Da-Wei ate } \tfrac{5}{12} \text{ of a pizza.}$$

$$\text{Mr. Gomez ate } \tfrac{5}{6} \text{ of a pizza.}$$

a. How many pizzas did they eat? Write a number sentence to support your answer.

b. How many pizzas were left? Write a number sentence to support your answer.

5. For parts (a)–(d), find each sum or difference. Show all your work.

a. $\frac{2}{3} + \frac{4}{5}$ **b.** $3\frac{2}{3} + 7\frac{3}{8}$

c. $\frac{3}{4} - \frac{2}{5}$ **d.** $10\frac{2}{3} - 8\frac{9}{12}$

Partner Quiz

1. Bob is making treat bags for his daughter's birthday party. He decided to use the recipe below for each bag. He needs to make 6 bags so each friend can have one and he wants to make $\frac{1}{2}$ bag for his two-year-old to have as well. How much of each ingredient will he need to make the $6\frac{1}{2}$ bags? Write number sentences to support your answer.

Recipe for 1 Bag

$\frac{1}{3}$ cup peanuts

$\frac{3}{4}$ cup pretzels

$\frac{1}{5}$ cup raisins

$\frac{2}{3}$ cup popcorn

2. On a particular map of Denmark, 1 inch on the map represents 12 miles.

 = **12 Miles**

   a. What does $2\frac{1}{2}$ inches on the map represent? Write a number sentence and show your work.

   b. What does $3\frac{3}{4}$ inches on the map represent? Write a number sentence and show your work.

Partner Quiz *(continued)*

3. Caroline had a pan of lasagna $\frac{3}{4}$ full. She had some friends over for lunch and the friends ate $\frac{2}{3}$ of the pan of lasagna.

   a. How much of the pan of lasagna did her friends eat? Use a drawing and a number sentence to support your answer.

   b. Savannah had a lasagna pan $\frac{2}{3}$ full. She had friends over for lunch and they ate $\frac{3}{4}$ of the pan of lasagna. How is this different from what happened with Caroline's pan of lasagna?

   c. How is this the same as what happened with Caroline's pan of lasagna?

4. Write a story problem to fit the computation below. Explain why the calculation matches the story.

$$1\frac{2}{3} \times \frac{1}{4}$$

Multiple-Choice Items

1. Which picture shows that $\frac{2}{3}$ of the 6 circles are shaded?

   A. ● ● ○ ○ ○ ○   **B.** ● ○ ● ○ ● ○

   C. ● ● ○ ○ ● ●   **D.** ● ● ● ● ● ○

2. An airplane flew at an average speed of 432 miles per hour for $2\frac{1}{2}$ hours. How far did the plane fly?

   F. 10.8 miles   **G.** 108 miles   **H.** 1,080 miles   **J.** 10,800 miles

3. Shrya needed 3 cups of flour for a recipe. She could only find a $\frac{1}{4}$-cup measuring cup. How can she figure out how many times she must fill a $\frac{1}{4}$-cup measuring cup to get 3 cups?

   A. Add 3 and $\frac{1}{4}$.   **B.** Subtract $\frac{1}{4}$ from 3.

   C. Multiply 3 by $\frac{1}{4}$.   **D.** Divide 3 by $\frac{1}{4}$.

4. $\frac{3}{7} \div \frac{4}{7} = \blacksquare$

   F. $\frac{12}{49}$ **G.** $\frac{3}{4}$ **H.** $1\frac{1}{3}$ **J.** $1\frac{5}{7}$

5. $\frac{1}{6} + \frac{1}{9} = \blacksquare$

   A. $\frac{1}{3}$ **B.** $\frac{5}{18}$ **C.** $\frac{2}{9}$ **D.** $\frac{2}{15}$

6. $3\frac{1}{2} \times 4\frac{1}{2} = \blacksquare$

   F. $15\frac{3}{4}$ **G.** 14   **H.** $13\frac{1}{2}$ **J.** $12\frac{1}{4}$

7. $2\frac{1}{4} - \frac{7}{8} = \blacksquare$

   A. $3\frac{1}{8}$ **B.** $2\frac{5}{8}$ **C.** $1\frac{5}{8}$ **D.** $1\frac{3}{8}$

Multiple-Choice Items (continued)

8. Carletta bought 14 yards of green string to make shoelaces in the school color for her basketball team. She estimates that it takes $\frac{2}{5}$ yard to make one shoelace. How many shoelaces can she make?

   F. $5\frac{3}{5}$ **G.** 28   **H.** 35   **J.** 42

9. Mr. Cisneros is cooking for an apple celebration. He uses $10\frac{3}{8}$ pounds of apples to bake pies and $5\frac{1}{4}$ pounds of apples to make applesauce. How many more pounds of apples does he use for the pies than for applesauce?

   A. $5\frac{1}{8}$ **B.** $5\frac{2}{8}$ **C.** $15\frac{1}{8}$ **D.** $15\frac{5}{8}$

10. There are 32 students in Ms. Keusch's homeroom. Of the students, $\frac{3}{8}$ are boys. How many boys are in her homeroom?

   F. 6   **G.** 8   **H.** 12   **J.** 14

11. In the refrigerator, Teguh found $\frac{3}{4}$ of a pizza. He ate $\frac{1}{6}$ of what was left. How much of the pizza did he eat?

   A. $\frac{1}{24}$ **B.** $\frac{1}{8}$ **C.** $\frac{1}{4}$ **D.** $\frac{1}{3}$

12. Grace has a bag of three different kinds of cookies. $\frac{2}{9}$ of the cookies have chocolate chips and $\frac{1}{3}$ of the cookies have oatmeal and raisins. How many of the cookies have chocolate chips or oatmeal and raisins?

   F. $\frac{2}{27}$ **G.** $\frac{1}{9}$ **H.** $\frac{5}{9}$ **J.** $\frac{2}{3}$

Name _____ Date _____ Class _____

Notebook Checklist

Place a ✓ next to each item you have completed.

Notebook Organization

_____ Problems and Mathematical Reflections are labeled and dated.

_____ Work is neat and easy to find and follow.

Vocabulary

_____ All words are listed.   _____ All words are defined or described.

Assessments

_____ Check-Up   _____ Partner Quiz

_____ Unit Test

Assignments

_____ _____   _____ _____

_____ _____   _____ _____

_____ _____   _____ _____

_____ _____   _____ _____

_____ _____   _____ _____

_____ _____   _____ _____

_____ _____   _____ _____

_____ _____   _____ _____

_____ _____   _____ _____

_____ _____   _____ _____

_____ _____   _____ _____

_____ _____   _____ _____

_____ _____   _____ _____

_____ _____   _____ _____

Self Assessment

Mathematical Ideas

After studying the mathematics in *Bits and Pieces II*:

1. a. I learned these things about numbers and their properties:

b. Here are page numbers of notebook entries that give evidence of what I have learned, along with descriptions of what each entry shows:

2. a. These are the mathematical ideas that I am still struggling with:

b. This is why I think these ideas are difficult for me:

c. Here are page numbers of notebook entries that give evidence of what I am struggling with, along with descriptions of what each entry shows:

Class Participation

I contributed to the classroom **discussion** and understanding of *Bits and Pieces II* when I ... (Give examples.)

Self Assessment *(continued)*

Learning Environment

Rate each learning activity listed below using this scale:

1 I consistently struggled to understand the mathematics and I'm still not sure that I understand it.

2 I struggled somewhat but now I understand more than I did.

3 I had to work, but I feel confident that I understand now.

4 I understood everything pretty easily and I feel confident that I know the mathematics in these problems.

5 Everything came easily. I knew most of the mathematics before we did this.

Learning Activities:

_____ Problems from the Investigations

_____ ACE Homework Assignments

_____ Mathematical Reflections

_____ Check-Up

_____ Quiz

_____ Looking Back and Looking Ahead

_____ Unit Test

Check any of the following that you feel are the most helpful in adding to the success of your learning.

❏ Working on my own in class

❏ Discussing a problem with a partner

❏ Working in a small group of 3 or 4 people

❏ Discussing a problem as a whole class

❏ Individual or group presentation to the whole class

❏ Hearing how other people solved the problem

❏ Summarizing the mathematics as a class and taking notes

❏ Completing homework assignments

Name _____ Date _____ Class _____

Unit Test

Write number sentences to support your answers.

1. A local newspaper, The Lansing Times, sells advertising space. It charges advertisers according to the fraction of a page their ad will fill.

a. A new restaurant owner purchased ads to be put in the paper over several days. She bought two $\frac{1}{5}$-page ads, nine $\frac{1}{20}$-page ads, and five $\frac{1}{4}$-page ads. What is the total amount of space that she bought? Write a number sentence to show your reasoning.

b. The Comfy Couch Furniture store purchased $3\frac{1}{5}$ pages to advertise upcoming sales for the summer. When they did not receive a shipment as planned, they were not ready for their Fourth of July sale and had to cancel the $1\frac{7}{10}$ pages they had purchased for advertising the sale. How many pages of advertising did the store use? Write a number sentence to show your reasoning.

Unit Test (continued)

2. Sammy's mother bought $2\frac{1}{2}$ pounds of blueberries on Monday. Sammy ate $\frac{1}{4}$ of the blueberries before he went to bed.

   a. How many pounds of blueberries did Sammy eat on Monday?

   b. How many pounds of blueberries were left over?

   c. On Tuesday, Sammy ate $\frac{1}{3}$ of the leftover blueberries. How many pounds of blueberries did Sammy eat on Tuesday?

   d. Did Sammy eat more blueberries on Monday or Tuesday? Explain your reasoning.

3. Sammy's mother also bought $3\frac{1}{3}$ pounds of strawberries to make strawberry smoothies. She estimates that she will need $\frac{1}{9}$ pound of strawberries for each smoothie. How many smoothies can she make with the strawberries she bought?

4. How many bows can you make from $3\frac{2}{3}$ meters of ribbon if a bow takes $\frac{1}{4}$ meter of ribbon?

Unit Test *(continued)*

For each number sentence, find the value of N. Show your work.

5. $N - \frac{1}{5} = \frac{7}{20}$

   A. $\frac{3}{20}$ **B.** $\frac{11}{20}$ **C.** $\frac{8}{25}$ **D.** $\frac{6}{15}$

6. $\frac{2}{3} \times N = 12$

   F. 8   **G.** 20   **H.** 6   **J.** 18

7. $N + \frac{3}{4} = \frac{19}{20}$

   A. $\frac{16}{16}$ **B.** $\frac{34}{20}$ **C.** $\frac{1}{5}$ **D.** $\frac{22}{24}$

8. $6 \div \frac{2}{3} = N$

   F. 2   **G.** 9   **H.** 4   **J.** 8

9. Find the sum of $1\frac{1}{3}$ and $\frac{5}{6}$.

10. Find the difference of $1\frac{1}{3}$ and $\frac{5}{6}$.

11. Find the product of $1\frac{1}{3}$ and $\frac{5}{6}$.

12. Find the quotient of $1\frac{1}{3}$ and $\frac{5}{6}$.

Question Bank

1. For parts (a)–(b), tell which sum or difference is larger. Show your work.

    a. $\frac{4}{5} + \frac{5}{8}$ or $\frac{4}{7} + \frac{5}{9}$

    b. $\frac{14}{12} - \frac{2}{8}$ or $\frac{10}{9} - \frac{2}{6}$

2. Gregorio made money over his summer vacation by mowing lawns. One week he worked the following schedule:

Monday	$5\frac{1}{2}$ hours
Wednesday	$4\frac{1}{4}$ hours
Thursday	$2\frac{3}{4}$ hours
Friday	$2\frac{3}{4}$ hours

    a. How many hours did Gregorio work for the week?

    b. He needs to work 20 hours to earn the money for a trip. Will he have enough after working just this one week? Explain.

3. Which sums are greater than $\frac{2}{3}$?

    a. $\frac{1}{8} + \frac{1}{6}$ b. $\frac{2}{12} + \frac{3}{9}$ c. $\frac{2}{6} + \frac{2}{18}$ d. $\frac{3}{6} + \frac{1}{4}$

4. Jin-Lee and Sarah decide to make a pancake breakfast for six people. They found a recipe that will make 12 silver-dollar pancakes per batch. They need 30 silver-dollar pancakes to give 5 per person. How much of each ingredient will they need to make 30 silver-dollar pancakes?

    Silver-Dollar Pancakes Recipe for 12 pancakes

$1\frac{1}{4}$ cups flour	$\frac{1}{2}$ teaspoon salt
1 egg	$\frac{3}{4}$ cup milk
3 teaspoons baking powder	2 tablespoons salad oil
$1\frac{1}{2}$ tablespoons sugar	

5. a. In stage A, the middle one-third of a line segment is covered by a triangle. What fraction of the line is covered at stage A? What fraction is *not* covered?

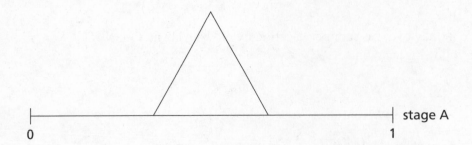

stage A

0   1

b. In stage B, the middle one-third of each of the two parts that were uncovered in stage A are covered. What fraction of the line is covered at stage B? What fraction is *not* covered?

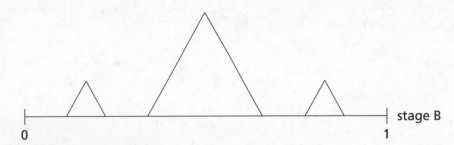

stage B

0   1

c. In stage C, the middle one-third of each of the parts that were not covered in stage B are covered. What fraction of the line is covered at stage C? What fraction is *not* covered?

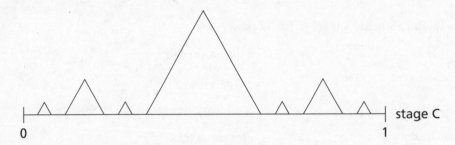

stage C

0   1

6. Students gave four answers to this exercise:

Write two fractions with a sum greater than $\frac{3}{4}$ but less than 1.

Which of the following answers is correct?

A. $\frac{1}{8} + \frac{2}{4}$ **B.** $\frac{1}{3} + \frac{2}{4}$ **C.** $\frac{3}{6} + \frac{2}{4}$ **D.** $\frac{1}{3} + \frac{1}{4}$

Check-Up

1. The squares on this grid are 1 cm long and 1 cm wide. Outline two different figures with an area of 12 sq cm and a perimeter of 16 cm.

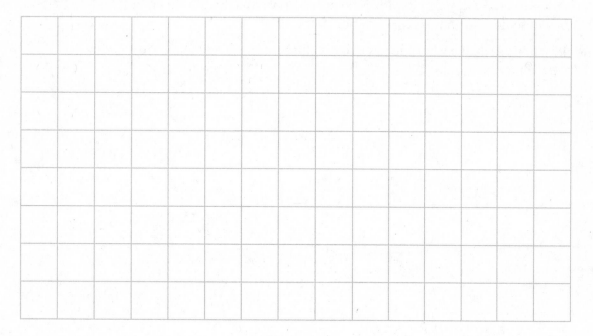

2. Find the area and perimeter of this rectangle. Explain how you found your answers.

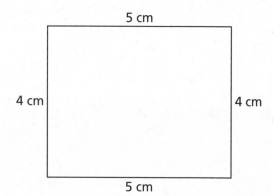

Check-Up (continued)

3. Because the winters are very windy and snowy for Sarah Fieldler, her mom decides to build a small snow shelter for her children to wait in before the school bus arrives in the morning. Mrs. Fieldler has only enough wood to build a shelter whose floor has a total perimeter of 20 feet.

   a. Make a table of all the whole number possibilities for the length and width of the shelter.

   b. What dimensions should Mrs. Fieldler choose to have the greatest floor area in her shelter?

   c. What dimensions should Mrs. Fieldler choose to have the least floor area in her shelter?

   d. Township building codes require 3 square feet for each child in a snow shelter. Which shelter from part *a* will fit the most children? How many children is this?

70

Partner Quiz

1. Ruanna was using cardboard to make mats for her photos. The photos were 3 inches by 4 inches. The mats were different sizes and different shapes.

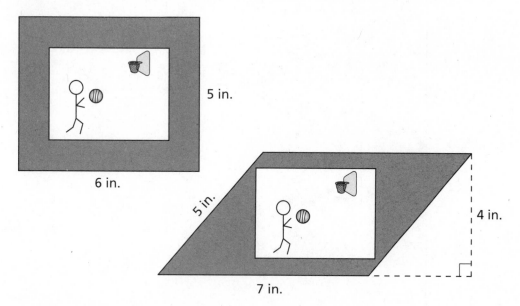

a. How much cardboard (in square inches) will be showing in the rectangular mat?

b. How much cardboard (in square inches) will be showing in the non-rectangular mat?

c. If she decided to put a narrow frame around each mat, how many inches of frame material would she need to surround each of the mats?

Partner Quiz (continued)

2. Use the diagram below to answer the following questions.

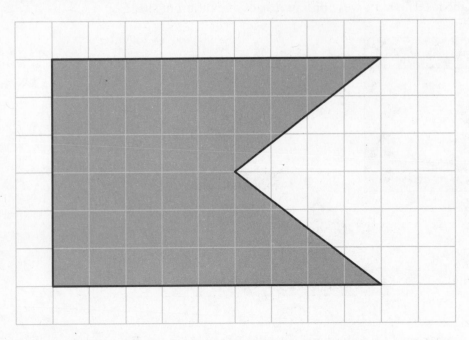

   a. What is the perimeter of the figure? Explain your reasoning and any strategies that you use.

   b. What is the area of the figure? Explain your reasoning and any strategies that you use.

3. Decide if each of the following statements is true or false. Explain your reasoning.

   a. Any two parallelograms with the same side lengths have the same area.

   b. Any two triangles with the same side lengths have the same area.

Multiple-Choice Items

1. What is the area of this triangle?

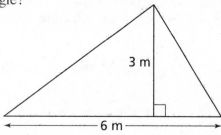

3 m

6 m

   A. 18 sq. m   **B.** 36 sq. m   **C.** 9 sq. m   **D.** 6 sq. m

2. Alexa wants to use ready-made 6-foot long fence sections for her yard. The yard is a rectangle with dimensions 30 feet by 36 feet. How many fence sections will she need to enclose her entire yard?

   F. 22   **G.** 132   **H.** 66   **J.** 120

3. A tire on Eduardo's car has a radius of 20 inches. What is the circumference of the tire to the nearest inch?

   A. 1256 in.   **B.** 63 in.   **C.** 126 in.   **D.** 400 in.

4. If the width of a rectangle is tripled, what will be the effect on its area?

   F. The area will remain the same.   **G.** The area will be 9 times as great.

   H. The area will be 3 times as great.   **J.** The area will be 6 times as great.

Multiple-Choice Items (continued)

5. Mahina calculated the circumference of a can she wants to decorate. She measured the diameter to be 6.4 in. What was the circumference of the can, to the nearest cm?

A. 39 cm   **B.** 40 cm   **C.** 20 cm   **D.** 36 cm

6. The figure below shows the dimensions of Aman's bedroom. Aman wants to put new carpet in the room. Which of the following will help him figure out how much carpet he needs? (All angles in the diagram are right angles.)

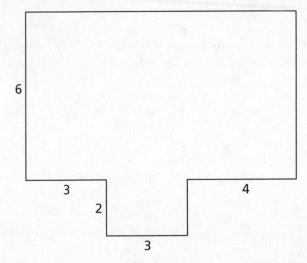

F $(6 \times 10) + (2 \times 3)$ **G.** $6 \times 3 \times 2 \times 3 \times 4$

H. $6 + 3 + 2 + 3 + 4$ **J.** $(6 \times 3) + (2 \times 3) + 4$

Multiple-Choice Items (continued)

7. What is the relationship between the area of the triangle and the area of the rectangle below?

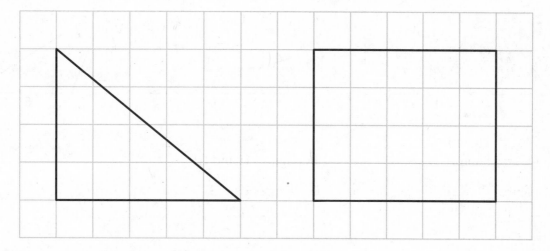

A. The area of the triangle is the same as the area of the rectangle.

B. The area of the triangle is half the area of the rectangle.

C. The area of the triangle is twice the area of the rectangle.

D. The area of the triangle is one-third the area of the rectangle.

8. What is the relationship between the perimeters of the triangle and the rectangle in Exercise 7?

F. The perimeter of the triangle is the same as the perimeter of the rectangle.

G. The perimeter of the triangle is less than the perimeter of the rectangle.

H. The perimeter of the triangle is greater than the perimeter of the rectangle.

J. We cannot know the relationship without measuring both perimeters.

Multiple-Choice Items (continued)

9. Which two figures below have the same area?

I 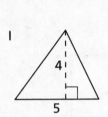 II 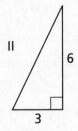 III 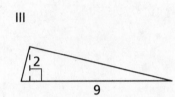 IV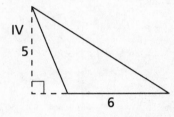

A. Figures I and II

B. Figures II and III

C. Figures II and IV

D. Figures I and IV

Notebook Checklist

Place a ✓ next to each item you have completed.

Notebook Organization

_____ Problems and Mathematical Reflections are labeled and dated.

_____ Work is neat and easy to find and follow.

Vocabulary

_____ All words are listed.   _____ All words are defined or described.

Assessments

_____ Check-Up   _____ Quiz   _____ Unit Test

Assignments

_____ _____   _____ _____

_____ _____   _____ _____

_____ _____   _____ _____

_____ _____   _____ _____

_____ _____   _____ _____

_____ _____   _____ _____

_____ _____   _____ _____

_____ _____   _____ _____

_____ _____   _____ _____

_____ _____   _____ _____

_____ _____   _____ _____

_____ _____   _____ _____

_____ _____   _____ _____

_____ _____   _____ _____

Self Assessment

Mathematical Ideas

After studying the mathematics in *Covering and Surrounding,*

1. a. I learned these things about area and perimeter:

b. Here are page numbers of notebook entries that give evidence of what I have learned, along with descriptions of what each entry shows:

2. a. The mathematical idea(s) that I am still struggling with are:

b. This is why I think these ideas are difficult for me:

c. Here are page numbers of notebook entries that give evidence of what I am struggling with, along with descriptions of what each entry shows:

Class Participation

I contributed to the classroom discussion and understanding of *Covering and Surrounding* when I . . . (Give examples)

Self Assessment (continued)

Learning Environment

Rate the learning activities using the following scale:

1   I consistently struggled to understand the mathematics and I'm still not sure that I know it.

2   I struggled somewhat but now I understand more than I did.

3   I had to work, but I feel confident that I understand now.

4   I understood everything pretty easily and I feel confident that I know the mathematics in these problems.

5   Everything came easily. I knew most of the mathematics before we did this.

_____ Problems from the Investigations

_____ ACE Homework Assignments

_____ Mathematical Reflections

_____ Check-Up

_____ Quiz

_____ Unit Test

Check the environments you feel are most helpful in adding to the success of your learning.

❑   Working on my own in class.

❑   Discussing a problem with a partner.

❑   Working in a small group of 3 or 4 people.

❑   Discussing a problem as a whole class.

❑   Individual or group presentation to the whole class.

❑   Hearing how other people solved the problem.

❑   Summarizing the mathematics as a class and taking notes.

❑   Completing homework assignments.

Unit Test

For problems 1–4, find the area and perimeter of each figure. (Figures are not to scale.)

1.

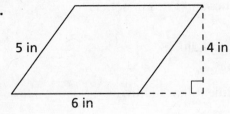

5 in 4 in

6 in

2.

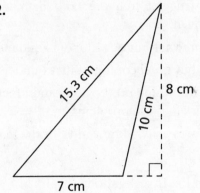

15.3 cm 8 cm

10 cm

7 cm

3.

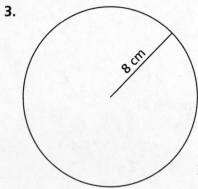

8 cm

4. (All angles in this diagram are 90°.)

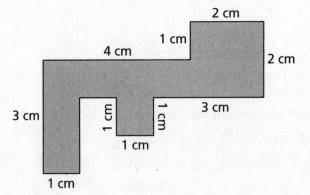

2 cm

1 cm

4 cm

2 cm

3 cm

1 cm

1 cm

3 cm

1 cm

1 cm

Unit Test (continued)

5. Suppose you built all the rectangles possible from 48 square tiles.

   a. Which rectangle would have the largest perimeter?

   Dimensions:

   Perimeter:

   b. Which rectangle would have the smallest perimeter?

   Dimensions:

   Perimeter:

6. Italiano's Pizza serves pizzas with diameters of 12 inches, 14 inches and 16 inches.

   a. How many square inches are in a 12-inch pizza?

   b. How many more square inches are in a 14-inch pizza than in a 12-inch pizza?

   c. DaVinci's Pizzeria serves a large square pizza, 15 inches on each side. Does this give more or less pizza than Italiano's large 16-inch diameter round pizza? How much more or less?

   d. Which has more crust along the outside edge of the pizza, DaVinci's large square pizza with 15 inches on each side or Italiano's large 16-inch diameter round pizza?

Unit Test (continued)

7. Below is a drawing of an ellipse on cm grid paper.

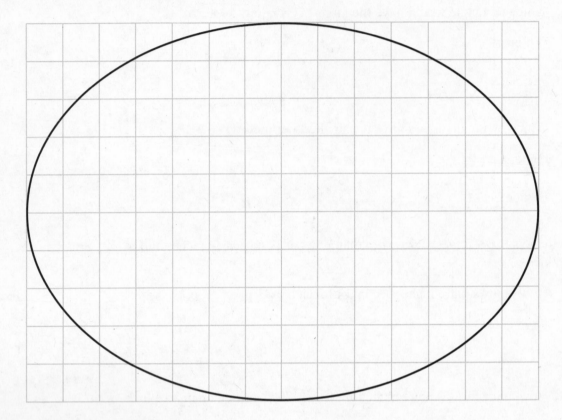

    a. Estimate the area of the ellipse.

    b. Describe the method you used to estimate the area. Is your estimate for area more or less than the exact area of the ellipse? Explain your reasoning.

Question Bank

Assign these questions as additional homework, or use them as review, quiz, or test questions. Grid paper, tiles, and transparent grids can be used as needed.

1. Jason is planning to redecorate his bedroom. He measured the room and made this rough sketch.

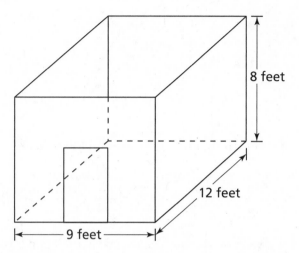

   a. Jason is planning to buy paint for the walls and ceiling. Will he need to find perimeter or area to figure out how much paint to buy? What unit of measure should he use?

   b. To determine how much new carpet to buy, will Jason need to find perimeter or area? What unit of measure should he use?

   c. Jason also needs baseboard for around the bottom of the walls. Will he need to find perimeter or area to figure out how much baseboard to buy? What unit of measure should he use?

   d. How much carpeting does Jason need? Show how you found your answer.

   e. How much baseboard does Jason need? Show how you found your answer.

   f. If a gallon of paint covers 350 square feet, how much paint does Jason need for the walls and ceiling?

2. Chad's dad wants to repaint the top of the step outside the front door with special paint that doesn't get slippery in the rain. At the right is a drawing of the top of the step. Each centimeter represents 1 foot.

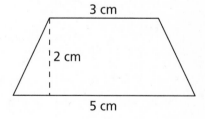

   a. Using the scale drawing, help Chad's dad by finding the area of the step. Keep a record of your work and sketches so you can convince him that you found it correctly.

   b. Each quart of paint covers 32 square feet. Chad's dad wants to apply two coats of paint. How many quarts of paint should he buy? Explain your answer.

3. Lydia's stepmother decided to paint the semicircular patio in their back yard. Here is Lydia's sketch of the patio, drawn on a grid. Each grid square represents 1 square foot.

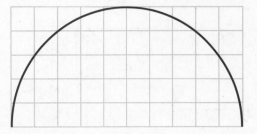

a. What is the area of the patio? Explain how you found the area.

b. Each quart of nonslip paint covers 32 square feet. How much paint should Lydia's stepmother buy if she plans to put one coat of paint on the patio? Keep a record of your work.

c. To keep grass from growing onto the patio, Lydia wants to plant a border around the patio. Since the patio is against the house, she only needs a border around the curved edge. How long will the border be? Show how you found your answer.

4. Shown below are the relative sizes of a large tile and a small tile. When measured with large tiles, the area of a rectangular room is 12 square units and the perimeter is 16 units.

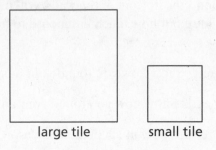

large tile   small tile

a. What would the area and perimeter of the room be (in tile units) if it were measured with the small tiles?

b. How do the measures you found in part (a) compare to the measures found by using the large tiles?

5. A neighbor asks you to help her design a rectangular pen for her dog, Ruff. Your neighbor has 42 meters of fencing to use for the pen.

a. What design would give Ruff the most space for playing?

b. What design would give Ruff the best space for running?

After looking at your designs, your neighbor decides to use her house as one of the walls for the pen. Her house is 35 meters long.

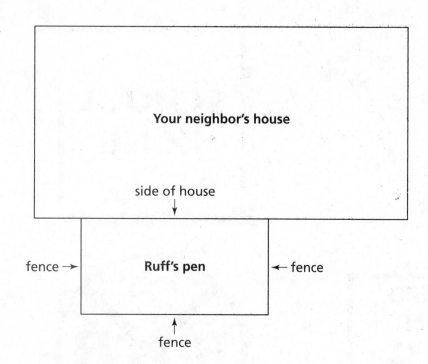

c. Using your neighbor's idea, now what design would give Ruff the most space for playing?

d. What design would give Ruff the best space for running?

6. The Acme sign company makes traffic signs for the state road commission. A model of the signs and their approximate measurements are given below.

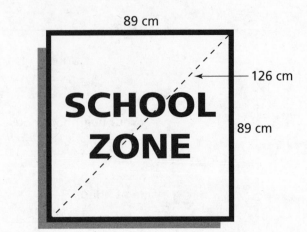

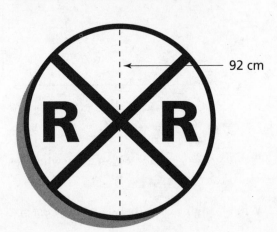

a. One of the costs that Acme must consider is the cost of metal. If metal costs $1.00 for every 1,000 square centimeters, what is the cost of the metal for each sign?

Yield sign: _____

School zone sign: _____

Speed limit sign:_____

Railroad crossing sign: _____

b. After the signs are cut, the edges must be sanded to prevent metal splinters. If the cost of sanding is 2 cents for every centimeter, what will it cost to sand each sign?

Yield sign: _____

School zone sign: _____

Speed limit sign:_____

Railroad crossing sign: _____

7. Lara is helping her family build a recreation room in their basement. The room will be 28 feet by 20 feet. They have already put up the walls.

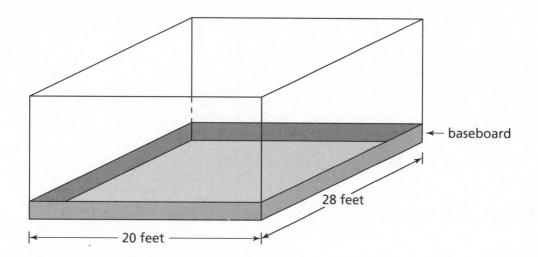

← baseboard

28 feet

20 feet

a. The family wants to tile the floor. Lara decides to buy 1-foot-square tiles. How many tiles will she need? Show your work.

b. The tiles Lara has chosen cost $.75 each. How much will the tile floor cost? Show how you found your answer.

c. Lara needs to buy baseboard to put along the wall. How much baseboard does she need? Show how you found your answer.

d. The baseboard comes in 10-foot and 16-foot lengths. How many boards of each length should Lara buy? Show how you found your answer.

When you encounter problems like this in the real world, you will often have to consider several factors. Questions (e)–(g) look at conditions that Lara might think are important.

e. Suppose these are the prices of the baseboard. How many boards of each length should Lara buy if she wants to spend the least amount of money? Explain your answer.

Baseboard	
16-ft lengths	$1.25 per foot
10-ft lengths	$1.10 per foot

f. When two sections of baseboard meet, they create a *seam*.

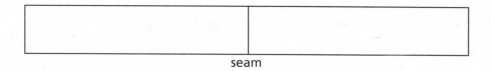

seam

If Lara wants as few seams as possible, how many baseboards of each length should she buy?

g. If you were Lara, how many baseboards of each length would you buy?

Check-Up 1

1. a. Estimate the following and explain how you made your estimate:

$$0.52 + 1.2 \qquad\qquad 4.4 - 1.29$$

b. For each problem in part (a), find the exact sum or difference.

2. a. Use fraction addition to find this sum: $1.23 + 3.9$

b. Use decimals and place value to find this sum: $2\frac{4}{10} + 3\frac{7}{100}$

3. Every night Dan's dad puts any pennies or nickels he has in his pocket into a container for Dan. Dan does not remove any money. Dave next door has the same arrangement with his mom. Here is the data from the third week:

Daily Cumulative Total for Week 3

	Monday	Tuesday	Wednesday	Thursday	Friday
Dave	$0.51	$0.68	$0.84	$1.26	$1.63
Dan	$0.72	$0.90	$1.02	$1.38	$1.76

a. Who had the most on Wednesday and by how much?

b. Who made the most over the week and by how much?

c. How much would Dan and Dave have if they combined their money on Friday?

Partner Quiz

1. Marie has three pieces of ribbon she wants to use to decorate a gift box. She measured the three pieces with a ruler and got 32.3 cm, 41.19 cm, and 57.8 cm. She needs 200 cm of ribbon for the box. How much is Marie over or under what she needs?

2. A winter sports pass at Wood Middle School costs $15. A student without a pass must pay $1.75 for each event. How many sports events would a student have to attend to make the pass a better deal?

Partner Quiz *(continued)*   *for use after* **Investigation 2**

Bits and Pieces III

3. Insert decimal points into the two factors, so that each of the following problems have different factors but give the same product. Explain how you made the problems.

Problem 1   Problem 2

$201 \times 15 = 30.15$ $201 \times 15 = 30.15$

4. Insert decimal points into the two factors so that each of the following problems give the correct product. Explain how you made the problems.

$111 \times 25 = 27.75$ $111 \times 25 = 277.5$

Check-Up 2

1. For each pair of problems, which computation gives the larger answer? Show
your work.

    a. $1.809 + 18.09$ or $7.05 + 11.918$

    b. $27.01 - 22.503$ or $5.021 - 0.514$

    c. 0.37×7.5 or 25.13×0.037

    d. $12.5 \div 0.25$ or $1.1 \div 0.02$

Check-Up 2 *(continued)*

2. Sam has to solve this computation problem: $3.05 \div 0.05 = ?$

   a. Write a story problem that would require the given division.

   b. What does the 3 in the number 3.05 mean in place-value terms?

   c. What does the 5 in the number 0.05 mean in place-value terms?

   d. Show how to write the problem as a fraction problem with common denominators and then find the solution.

   e. What does the solution to the division mean? (What does it tell you?)

Multiple-Choice Items

1. Four stores are having a sale on DVDs. Which store is offering the best deal?

    A. Store 1: $3 off the regular price of $18.99

    B. Store 2: 10% off the regular price of $18.99

    C. Store 3: 15% off the regular price of $18.99

    D. Store 4: $\frac{1}{4}$ off the regular price of $18.99

2. The Farwell girls' softball team went out to the local pizza restaurant to celebrate their victory. The bill came to $72. What would be the amount of a 15% tip on this bill?

    F. $7.20   **G.** $10.80   **H.** $9.00   **J.** $14.40

3. A group of students went to the grocery store. The students spent $15.20 altogether. Each student spent $1.90. How many students were in this group?

    A. 6   **B.** 7   **C.** 8   **D.** 9

4. Which division problem does **not** have the same quotient as $7.8 \div 3.9$?

    F. $78 \div 39$ **G.** $7.80 \div 3.9$ **H.** $0.78 \div 0.039$ **J.** $0.078 \div 0.039$

Multiple-Choice Items (continued)

5. Gabrielle bought 5 CDs. The individual cost of each CD was: $14.50, $13.95, $14.99, $12.75, and $16.95. The closest estimate to the total cost of the five CDs is:

A. $100   **B.** $50   **C.** $75   **D.** $80

6. During gym class, Troy jumped 4.5 feet. Brendon jumped 3.72 feet. How much further did Troy jump than Brendon?

F. 1.22 ft   **G.** 0.82 ft   **H.** 0.78 ft   **J.** 1.78 ft

7. Charissa stopped at a deli to buy lunch. She bought a turkey sandwich for $2.40, a bag of pretzels for $.70, and a lemonade for $1.10. How much did she pay for her lunch?

A. $4.00   **B.** $4.20   **C.** $5.00   **D.** $4.40

8. Which product is the smallest?

F. 0.3×0.4 **G.** 0.03×0.04 **H.** 0.3×0.004 **J.** 0.003×0.04

9. After which digit would the decimal be placed in the following product?

$$2.4 \times 51.44 = 123456$$

A. after the 1   **B.** after the 2   **C.** after the 3   **D.** after the 4

Multiple-Choice Items (continued)

10. How many decimal places are in the product of 3.76 × 42.89?

    F. 2   **G.** 3   **H.** 4   **J.** 5

11. How many decimal places are in the division of 3.75 ÷ 0.25?

    A. 0   **B.** 1   **C.** 2   **D.** 4

12. Which problem has the same quotient as 3.2 ÷ 14.5?

    F. 32 ÷ 14.5   **G.** 320 ÷ 145   **H.** 32 ÷ 145   **J.** 14.5 ÷ 3.2

Notebook Checklist

Place a ✓ next to each item you have completed.

Notebook Organization

_____ Problems and Mathematical Reflections are labeled and dated.

_____ Work is neat and easy to find and follow.

Vocabulary

_____ All words are listed.   _____ All words are defined or described.

Assessments

_____ Check-Up 1   _____ Check-Up 2

_____ Quiz   _____ Unit Test

Assignments

_____ _____   _____ _____

_____ _____   _____ _____

_____ _____   _____ _____

_____ _____   _____ _____

_____ _____   _____ _____

_____ _____   _____ _____

_____ _____   _____ _____

_____ _____   _____ _____

_____ _____   _____ _____

_____ _____   _____ _____

_____ _____   _____ _____

_____ _____   _____ _____

_____ _____   _____ _____

Self Assessment

Mathematical Ideas

After studying the mathematics in *Bits and Pieces III,*

1. a. I learned these things about percents and decimal operations:

    b. Here are page numbers of notebook entries that give evidence of what I have learned, along with descriptions of what each entry shows:

2. a. The mathematical ideas that I am still struggling with are:

    b. This is why I think these ideas are difficult for me:

    c. Here are page numbers of notebook entries that give evidence of what I am struggling with, along with descriptions of what each entry shows:

Class Participation

I contributed to the classroom discussion and understanding of *Bits and Pieces III* when I . . . (Give examples)

Self Assessment (continued)

Learning Environment

Rate the learning activities using the following scale:

1 I consistently struggled to understand the mathematics and I'm still not sure that I know it.

2 I struggled somewhat but now I understand more than I did.

3 I had to work, but I feel confident that I understand now.

4 I understood everything pretty easily and I feel confident that I know the mathematics in these problems.

5 Everything came easily. I knew most of the mathematics before we did this.

_____ Problems from the Investigations

_____ ACE Homework Assignments

_____ Mathematical Reflections

_____ Check-Up

_____ Quiz

_____ Unit Test

Check the environments you feel are most helpful in adding to the success of your learning.

❏ Working on my own in class.

❏ Discussing a problem with a partner.

❏ Working in a small group of 3 or 4 people.

❏ Discussing a problem as a whole class.

❏ Individual or group presentation to the whole class.

❏ Hearing how other people solved the problem.

❏ Summarizing the mathematics as a class and taking notes.

❏ Completing homework assignments.

Unit Test

1. Solve the following computations. Show your work.

   a. $11.46 + 32.917$

   b. $8.29 - 3.112$

   c. 12.3×4.2

   d. $36.8 \div 0.8$

2. Paul took a trip in May. The price of gasoline that he paid during his trip was $1.50 per gallon. He filled his van four times over the trip. The amounts he bought were: 15.082 gallons, 15.784 gallons, 14.804 gallons, and 15.331 gallons.

   a. How much gasoline did he buy on the trip?

   b. What was his total cost for gasoline on the trip?

   c. His odometer (measures distance traveled) read 23,451.1 miles when he pulled out of his driveway and 24,809.4 miles when he returned. How many miles did he travel on the trip?

Unit Test (continued)

3. If a toy store offers an additional 25% discount on board games that have already been reduced by 30%, will the final cost be the same as a discount of 55% on the original price? Work through an example to help explain your answer.

4. The total bill for drinks and a pizza for three people is $14.90 before tax.

   a. The sales tax is 5%. What will be the amount added to the bill for the sales tax?

   b. The group wants to leave a 15% tip on the cost of the food, not including the tax. What will be the amount added to the bill for the tip?

   c. How much should each person pay if they are to share the bill equally?

Unit Test (continued)

5. Suppose that your mom gives you $20 to go to the school supplies store. The state charges 6% sales tax on supplies. You need to buy the following items:

pencils	$ 1.29
notebook binder	$ 5.99
paper	$ 3.49
high-lighter pens	$ 2.35

a. How much will the supplies cost? Show your work.

b. Will you have enough money left to buy your favorite lunch that costs $5.39? Explain.

6. Ms. Sze is grading math tests. A student's work on a problem is given below:

$0.23 \times 2.07 = 0.04761$

Is the student correct? Explain.

Unit Test (continued)

7. Write a complete fact family for each problem.

    a. $12.4 - 3.2 = 9.2$ **b.** $3.2 \times 4.1 = 13.12$

8. The weight of an object is affected by gravity. Something that weighs one pound on Earth will weigh 1.08 times that on Saturn.

    a. If a rock weighs 3 pounds on Earth, what will it weigh on Saturn?

    b. If a rock weighs 3.24 pounds on Saturn, what will it weigh on Earth?

Question Bank

1. Troy is going to basketball camp. Before he goes, he needs to buy some things. He and his parents agree that he can buy two pairs of shorts, four t-shirts, six pairs of socks, and a jacket. Shop Easy has everything they need for the following prices:

   Shorts $7.98 each

   T-shirts $6.35—on sale: buy one at the regular price, and get a second at half price

   Socks $1.98 for two pairs

   Jackets $19.99 each

   a. How much will the total bill for Troy's clothes be, including sales tax? (Figure sales tax based on what is charged in your area.)

   b. Troy had $100 when he started shopping. Did he have enough money? If so, how much extra? If not, how much was he short?

2. Ms. Ngyen has a total of 150 students in her classes. Of these students, 30% eat during the first lunch period, 20% eat during the second lunch period, and the rest eat during the third lunch period. How many of her students eat during each lunch period?

3. Each week, Stewart saves $16 of his $48 paycheck. What percent of his pay does he save?

4. Ted has a coupon for 50¢ off a jar of Sticky peanut butter. If a jar of the peanut butter is priced at $1.59, what percent of the cost will Ted save by using the coupon?

5. The total bill for drinks and a large pizza for three people is $14.90 before tax. The sales tax is 5%. The group wants to leave a 15% tip. How much should each person pay if they are to share the bill equally? Indicate whether you figured out the tip before or after the tax was added.

6. Elizabeth is shopping for a new winter coat. She finds the coat she likes best in two different stores.

   - In the first store, the coat is priced at $84, but a sale sign states that the coat is $\frac{1}{3}$ off.

   - In the second store, the coat is priced at $76, but a sale sign states that the coat is $\frac{1}{4}$ off.

Store 1   Store 2

    $84 SALE $\frac{1}{3}$OFF $76 SALE $\frac{1}{4}$OFF

   a. From which store should Elizabeth buy the coat if she wants to spend the least amount of money?

   b. Elizabeth's mother finds the same coat in a catalog. The coat is priced the same as the regular price at the store from which Elizabeth has decided to buy [based on results to part (a)], but the catalog has the coat on sale for 30% off. In addition, Elizabeth's mother has a coupon for $5.00 off any purchase from the catalog. Any catalog order has a shipping charge of 6% of the price of an item. Which is the better buy, the coat at the store or the coat in the catalog?

7. Find out the rate of your local tax. Ingrid purchased a product in your area and was charged 63¢ for sales tax. Give three possible amounts the product could have cost.

8. The cost of renting a drum set is a $25 initial fee, plus $39.95 a month. How much will it cost to rent a drum set for a year?

9. Each solution is missing a decimal point. Correctly place the decimal into the solution. Explain how you decided where to place the decimal.

   a. $103.67 + 225.019 = 328689$

   b. $0.765 - 0.572 = 193$

   c. $3.84 \times 9.8 = 37632$

   d. $28.42 \div 8.9 = 32$

10. Use the decimal form of each fraction to find the solution. Show your work.

   a. $\frac{5}{8} + 1\frac{1}{2}$ **b.** $2\frac{3}{4} - 1\frac{2}{16}$ **c.** $4\frac{1}{8} \times 2\frac{1}{2}$ **d.** $3\frac{3}{4} \div 1\frac{1}{4}$

11. An airplane flew at an average speed of 432 miles per hour for 2.5 hours. How far did the plane fly?

12. Mr. Cisneros is cooking for an apple celebration. He uses 10.375 pounds of apples to bake pies and 5.25 pounds of apples to make applesauce. How many more pounds of apples does he use for pies than for applesauce?

13. There are 30 students in Ms. Keusch's homeroom. Of the students, 40% are boys. How many boys are in her homeroom?

14. In the refrigerator, Teguh found 75% of a pizza. He ate 50% of what was left. How much pizza did he eat?

   A. $\frac{1}{2}$ **B.** $\frac{1}{4}$ **C.** $\frac{3}{8}$ **D.** $\frac{3}{4}$

Check-Up

1. Rachel has tossed a fair coin ten times, and it has landed heads up every time.

   a. Is this possible? Explain.

   b. Is this likely? Explain.

   c. Which of the following statements is true about what will happen when Rachel tosses the coin again? Why?

     i. The coin will land heads up.

     ii. The coin will land tails up.

     iii. The chances of the coin landing heads up or tails up are equal.

     iv. The coin is more likely to land heads up.

     v. The coin is more likely to land tails up.

2. The probability of a particular event is $\frac{3}{8}$. What is the probability that the event will **not** happen? Explain.

3. Give an example of a situation with outcomes, which are not equally likely.

Check-Up (continued)

4. Which of the following numbers could **not** be the probability of an event? Explain.

$\frac{1}{3}$ 0 $\frac{8}{9}$ 1 $\frac{5}{4}$

5. Mandy has a bag containing one green block (G), one brown block (B), and one yellow block (Y). She conducted 20 trials in which she drew one block from the bag and then flipped a fair coin. Here are the results of her experiment:

G-T,   Y-T,   G-H,   G-T,   Y-H,   Y-T,   B-T,   Y-H,   G-T,   Y-T,

B-T,   Y-H,   B-T,   Y-T,   Y-T,   B-T,   G-H,   G-T,   Y-H,   Y-T

    a. What is the experimental probability of drawing the brown block and flipping heads?

    What is the theoretical probability?

    b. What is the experimental probability of drawing the yellow block and flipping tails?

    What is the theoretical probability?

    c. How would you explain the differences you found between the experimental and theoretical probabilities?

Check-Up (continued)

6. a. Give an example of an event that has a 100% chance of happening.

    b. Give an example of an outcome that is impossible.

    c. If an event is impossible, what are the chances it will occur?

Partner Quiz

Your class has been asked by a game company to test their newest game, Toss 2 Chips. You and your classmates will be playing and analyzing the game. The company wants to know whether Toss 2 Chips is fair for all players.

Description of Toss 2 Chips

Materials: Two chips and a small cup

- One chip has an X on both sides.
- One chip has an X on one side and a Y on the other side.

Rules:
1. Shake the chips in the cup and then pour them out.
2. Award points according to what shows on the chips. *It does not matter who tossed the chips.*
   - Player A gets a point if the chips match.
   - Player B gets a point if the chips do not match.

1. From the description of the game, do you and your partner think Toss 2 Chips is a fair game of chance? Explain your answer.

Play the game 20 times. Tally your results below.

Player A (match)	Player B (no match)

2. From your results, do you think the game is fair? Explain your reasoning.

Partner Quiz (continued)

Your teacher will set up a master chart on the board. Record your results—the number of matches and the number of non-matches—on the chart. After all partners have recorded their data, examine the entire class's results.

3. Based on the class's results, do you now think Toss 2 Chips is a fair game? Explain.

4. Would you rather rely on your own data or the entire class's data to decide whether the game is fair? Explain.

Multiple-Choice Items

1. Lisa has a set of 10 cards, numbered 1 through 10. If she picks a card at random, what is the probability that the card will be an 8?

A. $\frac{8}{10}$ **B.** $\frac{1}{5}$ **C.** $\frac{1}{10}$ **D.** $\frac{1}{4}$

2. Justine has a bag with 12 blue marbles, 6 green marbles, 8 purple marbles, and 4 red marbles. If she wants the probability of picking a blue marble to be $\frac{1}{2}$, what should Justine do?

  F. Add 2 green, 2 purple, and 2 red marbles

  G. Add 2 blue marbles

  H. Remove 1 green, 1 purple, and 1 red marble

  J. Add 6 blue marbles

3. When Brendan deposits a penny in his candy machine, out comes a gumball. Inside his gumball machine there are 6 blue gumballs, 6 red, 6 yellow, and 6 white. What are the chances he will get a blue gumball when he deposits his penny?

  A. 1 out of 24   **B.** 1 out of 6   **C.** 1 out of 4   **D.** 1 out of 12

4. In a survey of 100 students about their favorite pizza topping, 25 chose pineapple. According to these results, if a student is picked at random at the school, what is the chance that the student prefers pineapple as a pizza topping?

  F. 1 out of 5   **G.** 1 out of 4   **H.** 1 out of 2   **J.** 1 out of 6

Multiple-Choice Items (continued)

5. A penny is tossed and a number cube is rolled. What is the probability that the penny lands heads up and a five is rolled?

    A. 1 out of 2   **B.** 2 out of 12   **C.** 1 out of 8   **D.** 1 out of 12

6. Each box holds a set number of marbles. In each box, there is only one purple marble. Without looking, you are to pick a marble out of one of the boxes. Which box would give you the greatest chance of picking a purple marble?

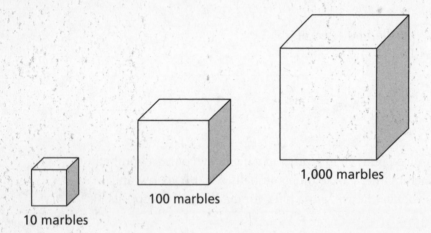

10 marbles   100 marbles   1,000 marbles

    F. The box with 10 marbles   **G.** The box with 100 marbles

    H. The box with 1000 marbles   **J.** It makes no difference

7. Ben and Lillie are going to roll a number cube one time to decide who will start a game. Which of the following is not a fair way to decide who will go first?

    A. If the value is even Ben goes first. If the value is odd Lillie will go first.

    B. If a 1, 4 or 6 is rolled Ben will go first. If a 2, 3, or 5 is rolled Lillie will go first.

    C. If the number is composite Ben will go first. If the number is prime Lillie will go first.

    D. If the number rolled is less than 3, Ben will go first. If the number rolled is greater than 3, Lillie will go first.

Notebook Checklist

Place a ✓ next to each item you have completed.

Notebook Organization

_____ Problems and Mathematical Reflections are labeled and dated.

_____ Work is neat and easy to find and follow.

Vocabulary

_____ All words are listed.   _____ All words are defined or described.

Assessments

_____ Check-Up   _____ Quiz   _____ Unit Test

Assignments

_____ _____   _____ _____

_____ _____   _____ _____

_____ _____   _____ _____

_____ _____   _____ _____

_____ _____   _____ _____

_____ _____   _____ _____

_____ _____   _____ _____

_____ _____   _____ _____

_____ _____   _____ _____

_____ _____   _____ _____

_____ _____   _____ _____

_____ _____   _____ _____

_____ _____   _____ _____

_____ _____   _____ Date _____

Self Assessment

Mathematical Ideas

After studying the mathematics in *How Likely Is It?*:

1. a. I learned these things about probability:

   b. Here are page numbers of notebook entries that give evidence of what I have learned, along with descriptions of what each entry shows:

2. a. The mathematical idea(s) that I am still struggling with are:

   b. This is why I think these ideas are difficult for me:

   c. Here are page numbers of notebook entries that give evidence of what I am struggling with, along with descriptions of what each entry shows:

Class Participation

I contributed to the classroom discussion and understanding of *How Likely Is It?* when I . . . (Give examples)

Self Assessment (continued)

Learning Environment

Rate the learning activities using the following scale:

1 I consistently struggled to understand the mathematics and I'm still not sure that I know it.

2 I struggled somewhat but now I understand more than I did.

3 I had to work, but I feel confident that I understand now.

4 I understood everything pretty easily and I feel confident that I know the mathematics in these problems.

5 Everything came easily. I knew most of the mathematics before we did this.

_____ Problems from the Investigations

_____ ACE Homework Assignments

_____ Mathematical Reflections

_____ Check-Up

_____ Quiz

_____ Unit Test

Check the environments you feel are most helpful in adding to the success of your learning.

❑ Working on my own in class.

❑ Discussing a problem with a partner.

❑ Working in a small group of 3 or 4 people.

❑ Discussing a problem as a whole class.

❑ Individual or group presentation to the whole class.

❑ Hearing how other people solved the problem.

❑ Summarizing the mathematics as a class and taking notes.

❑ Completing homework assignments.

Unit Test

Your class has been asked by a game company to test their new, exciting chip game, Toss 3 Chips. You will be playing and analyzing the game. The company wants to know whether the game is fair for all players.

Description of Toss 3 Chips

Materials: Three chips and a small cup

- One chip has an **X** on one side and a **Y** on the other side.
- One chip has an **X** on one side and a **Z** on the other side.
- One chip has a **Y** on one side and a **Z** on the other side.

Rules:
1. Shake the chips in the cup and then pour them out.
2. To score, award points by what shows on the chips. *It does not matter who tossed the chips.*
- Player A gets a point if any two chips match.
- Player B gets a point if all three chips are different.

Play the game 20 times. Tally your results below.

Player A (2 chips match)	Player B (no chips match)

1. From your results, do you think the game is fair? Explain your reasoning.

Unit Test (continued)

2. Your teacher will set up a master chart on the board. Record your results (the number of two chips matching and the number of no chips matching) on the chart. After all students have recorded their results, examine the entire class's results.

    a. From the class's results, what is the experimental probability of two chips matching?

    b. From the class's results, what it the experimental probability of no chips matching?

    c. Based on the class's results, do you think Toss 3 Chips is a fair game? Explain.

3. **a.** What is the theoretical probability of two chips matching?

    b. What is the theoretical probability of no chips matching?

    c. How do the theoretical probabilities in 3(a) and 3(b) compare with the class's experimental probabilities in 2(a) and 2(b)? Explain.

    d. Based on the theoretical probability, is Toss 3 Chips is a fair game? Explain.

Unit Test (continued)

4. A bag contains one green marble, two yellow marbles, four blue marbles, and five red marbles.

a. What is the probability of randomly drawing a blue marble from the bag?

b. If you double the number of green, yellow, blue, and red marbles in the bag, what will be the probability of drawing a blue marble?

c. Compare your answers for part (a) and (b). Are they the same or different? Explain.

d. How many blue marbles would you need to add to the *original* bag of marbles to make the probability of drawing a blue marble $\frac{1}{2}$? Explain your reasoning.

Unit Test (continued)

5. A gum machine contains orange, yellow, and purple gum balls. The probability of getting an orange gum ball is $\frac{3}{4}$. The probability of getting a yellow gum ball is $\frac{1}{6}$.

a. What is the probability of getting a purple gumball? Explain how you determined your answer.

b. If there are 36 gumballs in the machine, how many are purple? How many are yellow? How many are orange?

6. Use the spinner below to answer the following questions.

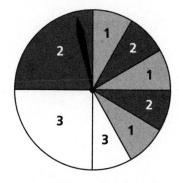

a. When you spin the pointer, are the three possible outcomes—landing on a one, two or three—equally likely? Explain.

b. If you were to spin the pointer 120 times, how many times would you expect to land on two?

Question Bank

Assign these questions as additional homework, or use them as review, quiz, or test questions.

1. **a.** Design a game (other than the Roller Derby game in your book) that uses two number cubes. Explain the rules, and give the number of players and the materials needed.

   b. Is your game a fair game of chance? Why or why not?

   c. Make up and answer at least two probability questions about your game.

2. Each box of Cocoa Blast cereal includes a Mad Mongo Monster action figure. There are four different action figures, and each figure has an equal chance of being put in a cereal box at the factory. Kalvin is trying to collect at least one of each figure. How many boxes of cereal do you think Kalvin will need to buy before he collects one of each figure? Find a way to investigate this question. Explain your methods and your reasoning.

3. John is going to toss three coins.

   a. What is the probability that all three coins will match? Explain your answer.

   b. What is the probability that there will be *at least two* heads? Explain your answer.

4. Design a bag containing 20 of the same object, such as blocks or marbles, in three or four different colors.

   a. Describe the contents of the bag you designed.

   b. Determine the theoretical probability of drawing each color by analyzing the contents of the bag.

5. **a.** How many different ways are there to answer a true/false test that has four questions?

   b. If you were to guess at the four answers for the true/false test, what is the probability of getting all four right?

   c. If you were to guess at the four answers for the true/false test, what is the probability of getting *at least two* right?

6. You have been saving your money for a year and now have enough to buy a new bike. You want to make an informed decision, so you go to the library and read a recent magazine with an article on models and makes of bikes. (The magazine makes recommendations of what would be the best product to buy, based on a sampling of hundreds of owners – in this case, bike owners.)

   You also decide to talk to a few of your friends who have bought new bikes in the last year. Four of your friends like a certain model of bike that the magazine article did not highly recommend. Three other friends each recommended the model of bike that they own.

   a. Would you go with the magazine's recommendation, your four friends' recommendation, or an individual friend's recommendation?

   b. Explain your reasons for deciding whose recommendation you would follow.

7. Here are the results from the coin-toss experiment, Problem 1.1, for one class of 30 students for 10 days. They each toss a coin once.

   a. Which days seem to have the most unexpected results?

   b. Complete the table and make a graph to show how the accumulated percent of heads changes from day to day.

Day	Number of Heads	Accumulated Percent Heads
June 1	14	$\frac{14}{30} \approx 46.66\%$
June 2	11	$\frac{25}{60} \approx 41.66\%$
June 3	20	
June 4	16	
June 5	19	
June 6	16	
June 7	11	
June 8	10	
June 9	16	
June 10	18	

8. Ms. Phillips' science students are trying to decide whether to get a rabbit, a hamster, an iguana, or a tarantula for their classroom pet.

 a. Make two suggestions of how to make a fair decision.

 b. Choose one of the animals you think that Ms. Phillips' class should select. Make a suggestion of how to make the decision where there will be a greater chance for this pet to be chosen. Explain how this suggestion increases the chances of your animal being selected.

9. Suppose that Aisha, Billie, and Caitlin play a game in which a nickel and a dime are tossed. If neither coin shows heads up, Aisha wins; if two coins show heads up, Billie wins; if one coin shows heads up, Caitlin wins. Caitlin says that this is a fair game because each player has a chance to win.

 a. How would you convince her otherwise?

 b. What would you say to Caitlin if each player has one win in the first three plays and she says, "See, the game is fair"?

10. Use this circle to draw a spinner with six sections. Make the spinner so that it is equally likely that the spinner will land in each of the six sections. What fraction of the circle is each section?

11. Use this circle to draw another spinner with six sections, but make this spinner so that it is **not** equally likely that the spinner will land in each of the six sections. What fraction of the circle is each section?

12. Two coins are tossed. Alan gets a point if the coins match, and Sondra gets a point if the coins do not match. Which of the following statements is true?

a. Alan is more likely to win.

b. Sondra is more likely to win.

c. Alan and Sondra have the same chances of winning.

d. There is not enough information to decide the chances of either player winning.

e. Sondra can never win.

Explain your answer.

13. If two number cubes are rolled over and over again, what sum would you expect to occur most often? Explain.

14. Josh is tossing beanbags randomly onto this game mat. What is the probability of a beanbag landing in an area marked B?

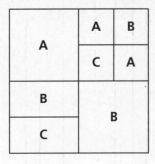

15. a. What is the probability of the pointer landing in a region marked A?

   b. What is the probability of the pointer landing in a region marked B?

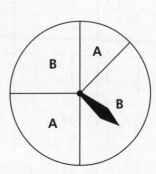

16. Fifty students in King Middle School were surveyed about their favorite sandwich. Here are the results of the survey:

Sandwich Preferences	
Peanut butter	32
Bologna	10
Cheese	7
Tuna fish	1

a. If a student is picked at random from the school, what is the probability that the student's favorite sandwich is peanut butter?

b. If a student is picked at random from the school, what is the probability that the student's favorite sandwich is **not** bologna?

c. If there are 550 students in the school, how many would you expect to say that cheese is their favorite sandwich?

17. A spinner is spun 100 times. The pointer landed on red 61 times and blue 39 times. How might the spinner be divided? Use the circle to draw a spinner that would be likely to give these results.

18. Which of the following numbers could not be the probability of an event? Explain your answer.

$\frac{1}{3}$ 0 $\frac{8}{9}$ 1 $\frac{5}{4}$

Check-Up

1. Consider each distribution below. For each distribution, where possible, tell how many people are represented by the data, and identify the mode and the median.

   a.

   Lengths of Last Names

   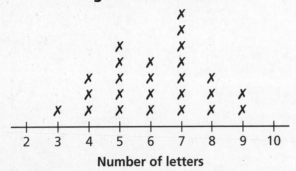

   Number of letters

   b.

   Birth Months

   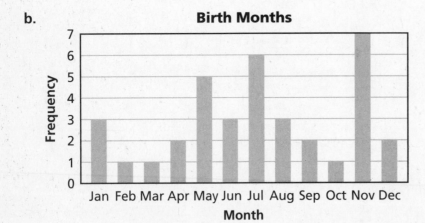

Check-Up

2. Make a line plot showing the lengths of 11 names so that the median length is 12 letters and the range is from 6 letters to 16 letters.

3. The media specialist in your school is planning a book fair. She is preparing a survey to ask students a few questions to help make the book fair a success.

   a. Write one question that will give the media specialist *numerical* data. Explain why she might want to know this information.

   b. Write one question that will give the media specialist *categorical* data. Explain why she might want to know this information

Partner Quiz

1. Fifteen students read the book *Gulliver's Travels*. In the book, the Lilliputians said they could make clothes for Gulliver by taking one measurement, the length around his thumb. The Lilliputians claimed that

   - the distance around Gulliver's wrist would be twice the distance around his thumb.
   - the distance around Gulliver's neck would be twice the distance around his wrist.
   - the distance around Gulliver's waist would be twice the distance around his neck.

   The students wondered whether this doubling relationship would be true for them, too. They measured the distance around their thumbs and their wrists in centimeters, then graphed the pairs of numbers on a coordinate graph. They drew a line connecting the points that represented wrist measurements that were twice thumb measurements.

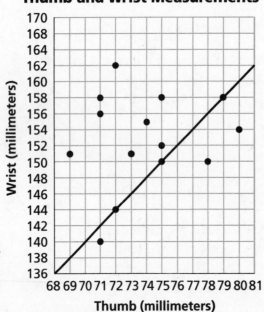

Thumb and Wrist Measurements

   a. How many students' measurements fit the Lilliputian rule that twice the distance around the thumb equals the distance around the wrist?

Partner Quiz *(continued)*

b. How many students' wrist measurements are less than twice their thumb measurements?

c. The point for Jeri's thumb and wrist measurements is above the line. If the cuffs of a shirt are twice the measurement around Jeri's thumb, how will the cuffs of the shirt fit her?

d. The point for Rubin's thumb and wrist measurements is below the line. If the cuffs of a shirt are twice the measurement around Rubin's thumb, how will the cuffs of the shirt fit him?

Partner Quiz (continued)

2. A group of students were curious about the changes in people's height over time. They gathered data about height from two different groups of students in their district: students in grade 5 and students in grade 8. The data they collected is shown in the table.

a. Organize and display these data using an appropriate graph or plot.

b. What is the typical height of a grade 5 students? Justify your answer.

c. What is the typical height of a grade 8 students? Justify your answer.

d. How does the distribution of height data from the grade 5 class compare with the distribution of height data of the grade 8 class?

e. There were three grade 8 students absent the day the data were collected. Their heights are 177 cm, 187 cm, and 163 cm. What happens to the mode and median when these new pieces of data are added to the data set?

Height (centimeters)

Grade 5	Grade 8
138	147
138	156
138	159
139	160
141	160
142	161
144	162
146	162
147	162
147	162
147	163
150	164
150	165
151	165
151	168
151	168
151	168
152	168
152	169
152	171
152	172
153	174
153	176
155	
155	
156	
156	
157	
158	
171	

Multiple-Choice Items

1. According to the graph, which country has about twice as many students choosing hockey as the favorite sport as the United States?

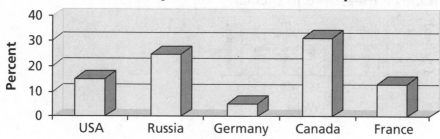

Hockey as Students' Favorite Sport

A. Russia **B.** Canada **C.** France **D.** Germany

2. Mrs. Nowak asked her students the following question:

If each number in a list is increased by 4, how does the mean of the new list compare with the mean of the old list?

Jim said: "The mean of the new list will be 4 times the mean of the old list."

Kara said: "The mean of the new list will be 4 points higher than the mean of the old list."

Ron said: "The mean of the new list will be four points lower than the mean of the old list."

Mae said: "There is no way to find out what the mean of the new list would be."

Which student answered correctly?

F. Jim **G.** Kara **H.** Ron **J.** Mae

Multiple-Choice Items

3. Farmers believe that 1 inch of rain per week is recommended for optimal crop growth. During which weeks would a farmer need to provide additional water?

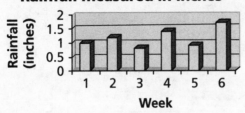

Rainfall measured in inches

A. Weeks 1 and 3

B. Weeks 4 and 6

C. Weeks 3 and 5

D. Weeks 1 and 5

4. The chart below shows the number of points Justine served in her first 6 volleyball games. Which of the statements is the *best* prediction of the number of points she will serve in Game 7?

Game	Points Served
1	4
2	3
3	4
4	6
5	5
6	4

F. She will probably serve 12 points

G. She will probably serve 2 points

H. She will probably serve 6 points

J. She will probably serve 4 points

Multiple-Choice Items (continued)

5. In 1996, a sports drink company came out with a new sports drink, Refuel. The graph below shows data on the new sports drink consumption. Which statement is a possible conclusion for the data?

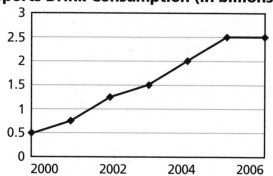

Sports Drink Consumption (in billions)

A. Consumption was greatest during the first year of introduction.

B. Consumption was greatest during the late 1990s.

C. Consumption will decrease in the mid-2000s.

D. Consumption leveled off from 2005 to 2006.

6. If the number of students tardy in all of Mr. Mariage's class continues to drop at a steady rate, predict how many students will be tardy during week number 6.

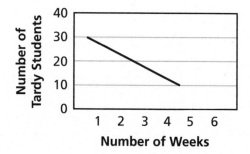

F. 32   **G.** 3   **H.** 10   **J.** 7.5

Notebook Checklist

Place a ✓ next to each item you have completed.

Notebook Organization

_____ Problems and Mathematical Reflections are labeled and dated.

_____ Work is neat and easy to find and follow.

Vocabulary

_____ All words are listed.   _____ All words are defined or described.

Assessment

_____ Check-Up   _____ Quiz   _____ Unit Test

Assignments

_____	_____	_____	_____
_____	_____	_____	_____
_____	_____	_____	_____
_____	_____	_____	_____
_____	_____	_____	_____
_____	_____	_____	_____
_____	_____	_____	_____
_____	_____	_____	_____
_____	_____	_____	_____
_____	_____	_____	_____
_____	_____	_____	_____
_____	_____	_____	_____
_____	_____	_____	_____

Self Assessment

Mathematical Ideas

After studying the mathematics in *Data About Us*:

1. a. I learned these things about collecting, displaying, and analyzing data:

    b. Here are page numbers of notebook entries that give evidence of what I have learned, along with descriptions of what each entry shows:

2. a. The mathematical idea(s) that I am still struggling with are:

    b. This is why I think these ideas are difficult for me:

    c. Here are page numbers of notebook entries that give evidence of what I am struggling with, along with descriptions of what each entry shows:

Class Participation

I contributed to the classroom discussion and understanding of *Data About Us* when I . . . (Give examples)

Self Assessment (continued)

Learning Environment

Rate the learning activities using the following scale:

1 I consistently struggled to understand the mathematics and I'm still not sure that I know it.

2 I struggled somewhat but now I understand more than I did.

3 I had to work, but I feel confident that I understand now.

4 I understood everything pretty easily and I feel confident that I know the mathematics in these problems.

5 Everything came easily. I knew most of the mathematics before we did this.

_____ Problems from the Investigations

_____ ACE Homework Assignments

_____ Mathematical Reflections

_____ Check-Up

_____ Quiz

_____ Unit Test

Check the environments you feel are most helpful in adding to the success of your learning.

❏ Working on my own in class.

❏ Discussing a problem with a partner.

❏ Working in a small group of 3 or 4 people.

❏ Discussing a problem as a whole class.

❏ Individual or group presentation to the whole class.

❏ Hearing how other people solved the problem.

❏ Summarizing the mathematics as a class and taking notes.

❏ Completing homework assignments.

Unit Test

1. A group of 9 students has these numbers of children in their families: 3, 2, 4, 2, 1, 5, 1, 2, and 7 children.

   a. Find the median number of children in the 9 families.

   b. Find the mean number of children in the 9 families.

   c. Explain what happens to the mean number of children when the family with 7 children adopts 5 more children.

2. Create two different groups of 5 students that have a mean of 3 children in their family.

Unit Test (continued)

3. The stem plot below shows test scores for Ms. McIntyre's class on a state
mathematics test. Students can score from 0 to 100 points.

Class Test Scores

```
0 | 5
1 |
2 | 4
3 | 4 9
4 | 3 7 8
5 | 7 9
6 | 1 6 8
7 | 3 5 6 8 8
8 | 1 2 2 2 5
9 | 0 3 9
```
Key: 8 | 1 means 81

a. What is the range of the data?

b. What is the median of the data? How many students had a score the same
as the median?

Unit Test (continued)

4. A class investigated the question of how many paces it takes to travel from their class to the gym. They measured the distance by counting the number of paces each student walked. Every step made on the right foot counted as one pace. Here are their results:

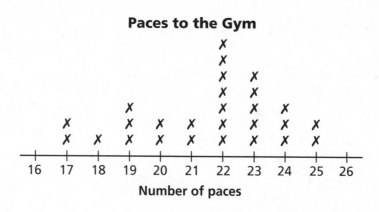

Paces to the Gym

Number of paces

a. What is the median number of paces the students took to travel the distance?

b. Make a bar graph that displays this information. Explain how the bar graph is similar to and different from a line plot.

c. Who has the shorter pace: the student who traveled the distance in 17 paces or the student who traveled the distance in 25 paces? Explain your thinking.

Question Bank

Assign these questions as additional homework, or use them as review, quiz, or test questions.

1. For the distribution below, tell how many people are represented and identify the mode, median, and range.

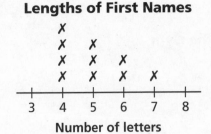

Lengths of First Names

Number of letters

2. Make a line plot showing the ages in years of 12 students so that the median age is 12.5 years and the difference between the highest age and the lowest age is 9 years.

3. The mean number of children in six families is 5 children.

   a. What is the total number of children in the six families?

   b. Other than six families of 5 children, create a set of families that fits this information.

   c. Would another classmate's set of families for question b have to be the same as yours? Explain.

4. In the story *The Phantom Tollbooth*, Milo is told that the average number of children in a family is 2.58. You know that a 0.58 boy or girl cannot exist. How can the calculations for the mean produce a number representing a child that does not seem to make sense?

5. Most people will walk about 158,125 kilometers in their lifetime, or around the world 4.5 times.

   a. How do you suppose this statistic was determined?

   b. What might you do if you were asked to investigate the question, "How far do most people walk in their lifetime?"

6. A class investigated how many pets each student in the class had. A number of students in their class had no pets at all. Here's how their data looked:

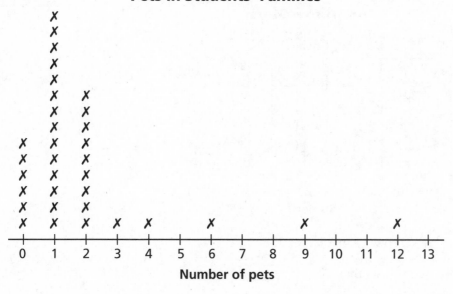

Pets in Students' Families

Number of pets

a. Would it be possible to have a data set for which the median number of pets for students is 0? Explain.

b. Would it be possible to have a data set for which the mean number of pets for students is 0? Explain.

7. In a survey of 7th grade girls at Saranac Middle School the favorite male actor was Brad Pitt. What statistical measure does this represent?

    A. mode   **B.** median   **C.** range   **D.** mean

8. Five students competed in a free-throw contest. The number of free throws out of 10 each student made is charted below. Based on the chart below, which of the following statements is false?

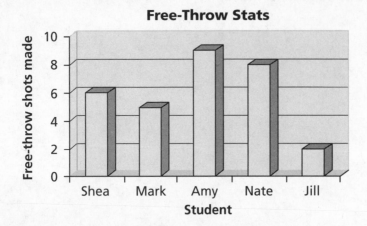

Free-Throw Stats

F. Amy made more free throws than Shea or Jill

G. Mark made more free throws than Jill

H. Nate made the most free throws

J. Shea made less free throws than Nate and Amy

9. The following data shows the high temperatures for a week in May in Michigan. What is the mean temperature for the week?

Day	Temp
Sun	66° F
Mon	67° F
Tue	71° F
Wed	68° F
Thurs	62° F
Fri	59° F
Sat	62° F

A. 62° F   **B.** 65° F   **C.** 68° F   **D.** 71° F

10. Students in 7th grade history classes are selling magazines to go on class trips. There are 6 different history class periods that are selling magazines. The graph below shows the number of magazines sold by students in the different class periods. How many more magazines were sold by class period 2 than class period 4?

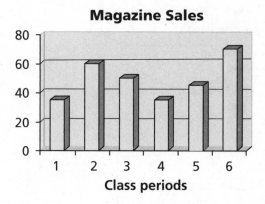

Magazine Sales

F. 15   **G.** 20   **H.** 30   **J.** 25

11. Using the magazine sales chart from question 10, which class periods sold fewer magazines than class period 5?

A. 1 and 3   **B.** 1 and 4   **C.** 2, 3, and 6   **D.** only 4

12. Mr. Nowak records the average number of chin-ups done by boys and girls in his gym class each year. The following graph shows Mr. Nowak's data for the past 7 years. How many more chin-ups did the average male do than the average female in 2001?

F. 5   **G.** 1   **H.** 3   **J.** 2

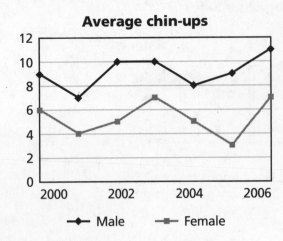

13. Using the chart in question 12, in which of the following years was the difference between the male's and female's chin-up count the least?

A. 1999   **B.** 2002   **C.** 1998   **D.** 2003

Prime Time Assessment Answers

Check-Up 1
1. 1, 2, 3, 4, 6, 8, 12, 24
2. 1, 31
3. 1, 5, 7, 35
4. 31; It has exactly two factors, one and the number itself.
5. 24, 35; These numbers have more than two factors.
6. **a.** 7, 14, 21, 28, 35, 49, 56
   b. Possible answers: 42, 63, 70, 77
7. The factors of 13 are 1 and 13. Both of these factors are not listed below the game board.

Check-Up 2
1. 25 and 36; Each of these numbers can be expressed as a number times itself. $5 \times 5 = 25$ and $6 \times 6 = 36$. If you made a tile model you could arrange each number of tiles into a square.
2. **a.** Factors of 16: 1, 2, 4, 8, 16
      Factors of 28: 1, 2, 4, 7, 14, 28
   b. **Factors of 16   Factors of 28**

   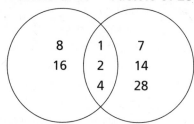

   c. 4
3. **a.** Multiples of 15: 15, 30, 45, 60, 75
      Multiples of 12, 24, 36, 48, 60
   b. **Multiples of 15   Multiples of 12**

   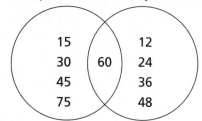

   c. 60
   d. Possible answers: 120, 180, 240, 300

4. Jill is incorrect. In order for 6 to be a common factor, both numbers must be divisible by 6. The number 56 cannot be divided evenly by 6.

Partner Quiz
1. **a.** 3, 4, 6
   b. 81
2. 36; If we consider an $a \times b$ rectangle to be different from a $b \times a$ rectangle, of the numbers 36, 37, 38, and 39, the number 36 gives nine choices of rectangles.
3. In 72 minutes, or at 4:12 P.M.
4. Judith could have 1, 2, 3, 4, 6, or 12 children at the party. These numbers are common factors of 24 and 36.

Multiple-Choice Items
1. C **2.** G **3.** D **4.** J **5.** D
6. J **7.** C **8.** F **9.** B **10.** H

Unit Test
1. Possible answers: 4×4; 2×8, $2 \times 2 \times 2 \times 2$
2. **a.** 72: $2^3 \times 3^2$
   b. 132: $2^2 \times 3 \times 11$
3. The number is $78 = 2 \times 3 \times 13 = 6 \times 13 = 3 \times 26$.
4. The number is 2,100. $2^2 \times 3 \times 5^2 \times 7 = 4 \times 3 \times 25 \times 7 = 2,100$
5. $1 \times 48, 2 \times 24, 3 \times 16, 4 \times 12, 6 \times 8$. List all the factor pairs, starting with 1 and 48, 2 and 24, etc., until you come to one that you have already used. For example, after matching 6 with 8, you move to 7 which is not a factor. The next number is 8 and you have already used it with 6, so you are finished.
6. 24 seconds
7. **a.** Carlos can make 32 sacks.
   b. Each sack would contain 3 small candy bars and 2 small popcorn balls.

8. a. 6
   b. Possible answers: 2 or 3
   c. 210
   d. Possible answers: 420, 630, 840
9. Odd; possible answers: $3^2 \times 5^2$ is equivalent to $3 \times 3 \times 5 \times 5$ or a string of odd factors. An odd number times and odd number is an odd number. This means that 3^2 is odd and 5^2 is odd, and when these two odd products are multiplied the final product will be odd.

Question Bank

1. Yes; the factors of numbers greater than 16 on the Factor Game board are between 1 and 15, so any number greater than 16 would be an illegal move because its factors are already circled.
2. Possible Answer: It is an even number. It can be divided by 2 without a remainder.
3. Possible Answer: It can be divided by 3 without a remainder.
4. Possible Answer: It can be divided by 5 without a remainder. It ends in 0 or 5.
5. 6, 12, 18, 24, 30, 36, 42, 48, 54, 60, 66, 72, 78, 84, 90, 96; Possible answers: They can be divided by 6 without a remainder. They have 6 as a factor. They are divisible by 2 and 3.
6. a. 225; to find all the factors of a number, you must check every whole number less than or equal to the square root of the number. If Mr. Matsumoto must check the numbers from 1 through 15, the number must be greater than or equal to 15^2, or 225, and less than 16^2, or 256.
   b. 255; as mentioned in the answer to part (a), the number must be less than 16^2, or 256. The greatest it could be is 255.
7. 11
8. Answers will vary.

9. a. 1, 4, 9, 16, 25, 36, 49, 64, 81, 100
   b.

Number	Factors
1	1
4	1, 2, 4
9	1, 3, 9
16	1, 2, 4, 8, 16
25	1, 5, 25
36	1, 2, 3, 4, 6, 9, 12, 18, 36
49	1, 7, 49
64	1, 2, 4, 8, 16, 32, 64
81	1, 3, 9, 27, 81
100	1, 2, 4, 5, 10, 20, 25, 50, 100

   c. 4, 9, 25, 49 (the squares of primes)
   d. 121
10. 81
11. a. 1, 2, 10, 20; If a number has 4 and 5 as factors, it must have the factors of 4 and 5 as factors; namely 1, 2, 4, and 5. It must also have the products of 2 and 5 and of 4 and 5 as factors, since these pairs of factors do not have any common factors.
   b. The smallest number is 20, because 4 and 5 do not have any common factors.
12. a. 6
   b. 12, 18, 24, 30, 36, 42, 48, 54, 60, 66, 72, 78, 84, 90, and 96
13. a. Ben bought four 9-ounce tubes. Aaron bought three 12-ounce tubes.
   b. The 12-ounce tube is the better buy at 9.6 cents per ounce. The 9-ounce tube cost 9.6 cents per ounce.

14. a.

15. Both are correct but Tyrone's is the accepted form. When we make a factor string, we use only prime factors. Otherwise, the strings could go on forever.

16. 120; the first three prime numbers are 2, 3, and 5. The first three composite numbers are 4 = 2 multiply 2, 6 = 2 multiply 3, and 8 = 2 multiply 2 multiply 2. The shortest string that contains the factors of all these numbers is 2 multiply 2 multiply 2 multiply 3 multiply 5. The smallest number that is divisible by all the numbers is the product of this string, which is 120.

17. The best move in this case would be 25, which gives your opponent only 5 points. **Note:** A prime number would be a bad move, since its only proper factor, 1, has already been circled.

18. Possible response: We played the Factor Game today. I discovered that it is best to go first and choose 29, the highest prime on the board, as your first move. After the first move, choose numbers like 25 that leave your opponent a small number of factors. Stay away from numbers like 30, which have many factors, until most of the factors are already circled.

19. a.

Number of bags	Number of cookies in a bag
1	36
2	18
3	12
4	9
6	6
9	4
12	3
18	2
36	1

b. Possible answer: Two cookies in a bag would be affordable and is a number a student would typically eat. This would also allow more students to buy cookies.

c. Possible answer: Each cookie cost $0.15 to make. They could be sold at $0.25 per cookie. So, a bag of one would cost $0.25, a bag of two would cost $0.50, ...

20. a. Alternate multiplying of terms by 2 and 3 to generate the next term.

b. 1,512 and 4,536

c. 7, since it is the only prime number in the sequence and is a factor of all the other terms in the sequence no matter how many terms are added.

21. a. Any two numbers that do not share a common factor (relatively prime numbers) will work. Examples are 3 and 4, 11 and 12, 15 and 8.

b. Any two numbers that share a common factor will work. Examples are 15 and 9, 10 and 25, 18 and 48, 45 and 8l.

c. If the numbers do not have a common factor, their least common multiple will be equal to their product. If the numbers have a common factor, their least common multiple will be less than their product.

22. a. $2 \times 2 \times 3 \times 3 \times 5 \times 5$, or written as $2^2 \times 3^2 \times 5^2$.

b. Answers will vary. Some possible answers: It is an even number. It is not an odd number. Nine is one of its factors. It is divisible by 15. It is not prime. It is composite because it has more than 2 factors. This is its one unique string of factorization (Fundamental Theorem of Arithmetic). It is a square number because you could group its prime factors to represent two of the same numbers multiplying themselves: $2 \times 3 \times 5$ multiplied by $2 \times 3 \times 5$ is the same as saying 30×30 or 30^2, which is 900.

Bits and Pieces I Assessment Answers

Partner Quiz A

1. $\frac{3}{4}$

2. from left to right: $\frac{1}{8}$, $\frac{2}{8}$ or $\frac{1}{4}$, $\frac{3}{8}$, $\frac{4}{8}$ or $\frac{1}{2}$, $\frac{5}{8}$, $\frac{6}{8}$ or $\frac{3}{4}$, $\frac{7}{8}$, $\frac{8}{8}$ or 1, $\frac{9}{8}$ or $1\frac{1}{8}$ (Figure 1)

3. **a.** Possible explanation: Julie would be right if her class goal was larger than Don's class goal and large enough so that $\frac{2}{3}$ of her goal was more money than $\frac{3}{4}$ of Don's. For example, If Julie's class goal was $300 and Don's class goal was $200, Julie's class would have raised $200 and Don's class would have raised $150.

   b. Possible explanation: Julie would be wrong if each class set the same money goal. If both classes had a goal of $300, Julie's class would have collected $200 and Don's class would have collected $225.

Check Up

1. **a.** $\frac{2}{4} < \frac{7}{12}$; Possible strategy: Using $\frac{1}{2}$ as a benchmark: "$\frac{2}{4} = \frac{1}{2}$ and $\frac{7}{12}$ is larger than half because you would need 6 pieces out of 12 to be equal to half"

   b. $\frac{5}{8} > \frac{6}{10}$; Possible strategies:
   Common Denominators: "I found common denominators and looked to see which numerator was larger. I knew that $\frac{25}{40} > \frac{24}{40}$.";

Common Numerators: "I made the numerators the same so I could compare the size of the pieces. $\frac{5}{8} = \frac{30}{48}$ and $\frac{6}{10} = \frac{30}{50}$. 48ths would be bigger pieces, then $\frac{30}{48}$ has to be the bigger fraction.";

One piece over Half: "Each fraction is one piece more than a half. Since $\frac{1}{10}$ is smaller than $\frac{1}{8}$, the $\frac{6}{10}$ is closer to a half or the smaller fraction."

   c. $\frac{8}{12} = \frac{10}{15}$; Possible strategies: Use common denominators or rewrite each fraction in lowest terms to see if they are equivalent. They may remember that the fractions are equivalent from work in the problems.

   d. $\frac{3}{8} > \frac{3}{12}$; Possible strategy: Since the numerators are equal, compare the size of the pieces. Eighths are cut into fewer pieces, so the piece size will be bigger, making it the larger fraction.

2. Possible answers: $\frac{2}{3}$, $\frac{5}{8}$, $\frac{9}{16}$, $\frac{11}{16}$, $\frac{6}{10}$, $\frac{53}{100}$, $\frac{17}{32}$, $\frac{23}{32}$, $\frac{712}{1,000}$

3.

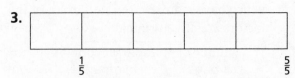

$\frac{1}{5}$ $\frac{5}{5}$

4. $1\frac{3}{4}$; $\frac{19}{10}$ or $1\frac{9}{10}$; $\frac{8}{3}$ or $2\frac{2}{3}$

Figure 1

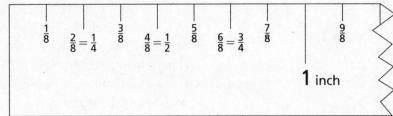

$\frac{1}{8}$ $\frac{2}{8} = \frac{1}{4}$ $\frac{3}{8}$ $\frac{4}{8} = \frac{1}{2}$ $\frac{5}{8}$ $\frac{6}{8} = \frac{3}{4}$ $\frac{7}{8}$ $\frac{9}{8}$

1 inch

Bits and Pieces I Assessment Answers *(continued)*

Partner Quiz B

1. (Figure 2)

2. The first fraction pair is incorrect. The last three are correct. Students may use fractions or decimals to help them reason about these problems. Possible explanation for $\frac{2}{3} < \frac{3}{4}$: Since $\frac{2}{3}$ falls between $\frac{1}{2}$ and $\frac{3}{4}$, it is less than $\frac{3}{4}$. Possible explanation for $\frac{65}{100} < \frac{3}{4}$: $\frac{65}{100} = 0.65$ which is less than 0.75 or $\frac{3}{4}$. Possible explanation for $\frac{14}{20} < \frac{3}{4}$: $\frac{14}{20} = \frac{7}{10} = 0.7$ which is less than 0.75 or $\frac{3}{4}$.

3. There are infinite answers possible. Some possibilities are: 0.471, 0.472, 0.473, 0.4711, 0.4777, or 0.479999.

4. $\frac{121}{22}$, 5.5

5. a.

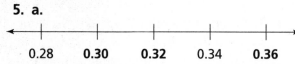

| 0.28 | **0.30** | **0.32** | 0.34 | **0.36** |

b.

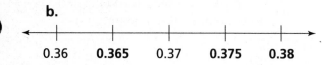

| 0.36 | **0.365** | 0.37 | **0.375** | 0.38 |

Multiple-Choice Items

1. C **2.** G **3.** D **4.** F **5.** C

6. J **7.** B **8.** G **9.** C **10.** F

Unit Test In-Class Portion

1.

	Fraction	Decimal	Percent
a.	$\frac{30}{100}$ or $\frac{3}{10}$	0.30 or 0.3	30%
b.	$\frac{20}{25}$ or $\frac{4}{5}$	0.80 or 0.8	80%
c.	$\frac{3}{4}$	0.75	75%
d.	$\frac{21}{40}$	0.525	52.5%

2. a. $\frac{16}{28}$ or $\frac{4}{7}$; about 57%

   b. $\frac{12}{28}$ or $\frac{3}{7}$; about 43%

3. a. 6%; Possible explanation: 6% is equivalent to 0.06.

   b. $\frac{1}{25}$; Possible explanation: $\frac{1}{25}$ is equivalent to 0.04 or 4%.

   c. 108%; Possible explanation: 108% is equivalent to 1.08 while 1.8 and $\frac{9}{5}$ are equivalent to 1.80.

4. a. $\frac{1}{10}$

   b. (Figure 3)

   c. 32

   d. 2.3 cm or 23 mm

Figure 2

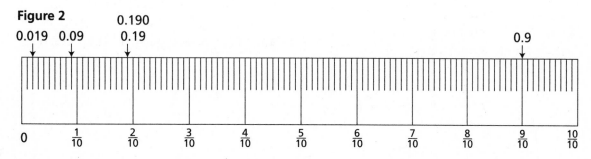

Figure 3

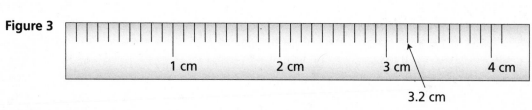

3.2 cm

5. 0.056, 0.060, 0.56, 0.6, 6.00

6. 20%

7. a. No, $\frac{3}{4}$ is equivalent to $\frac{9}{12}$.

   b. Yes, both are equivalent to $\frac{1}{2}$.

   c. Yes, $\frac{10}{8}$ can be written as $1\frac{2}{8}$ and $\frac{2}{8}$ is equal to $\frac{1}{4}$.

8. a. 11 thirds are in $3\frac{2}{3}$.

   b. 17 fourths are in $\frac{17}{4}$.

   c. nine fifths are in 1.8.

9. $\frac{8}{40} = \frac{2}{10} = 0.2$ or 0.20

10. a. 2.07

   b. 0.875

   c. 0.7

11. a. eight tenths

   b. four hundredths

   c. two and five hundred five thousandths

12. a. $\frac{8}{10}$ or any equivalent fraction

   b. $\frac{4}{100}$ or any equivalent fraction

   c. $2\frac{505}{1,000}$ or any equivalent fraction

Question Bank

1. a.

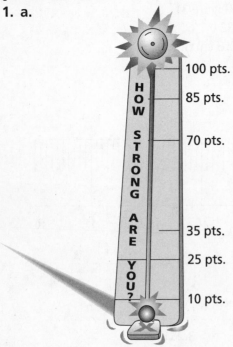

b. 10 is $\frac{10}{100}$ or $\frac{1}{10}$; 25 is $\frac{25}{100}$ or $\frac{1}{4}$; 35 is $\frac{35}{100}$ or $\frac{7}{20}$; 70 is $\frac{70}{100}$ or $\frac{7}{10}$; 85 is $\frac{85}{100}$ or $\frac{17}{20}$.

   c. 33 or 34 points   **d.** 60 points

   e. 25 points   **f.** 75 points

   g. Taylor should receive a few more points than Miki because $\frac{6}{9}$ of the way up the pole is more than $\frac{5}{8}$ of the way.

2. If you want the most pizza possible, join the first group. In the first group, you would share 6 pizzas among 4 people, so you would receive $1\frac{1}{2}$ pizzas. In the second group, you would share 8 pizzas among 6 people, so you would receive $1\frac{1}{3}$ pizzas.

3. a. $\frac{3}{12}$ or $\frac{1}{4}$ **b.** $\frac{5}{20}$ or $\frac{1}{4}$

   c. $\frac{2}{9}$ **d.** $\frac{7}{17}$

4. The muffins may not have been the same size to start with.

5. When comparing two decimal numbers that are both less than 1, you need to compare place-value amounts. For example, 0.37 is less than 0.6. This is because 0.37 means 37 hundredths or 3 tenths and 7 hundredths, and 0.6 means 6 tenths. Tenths are greater than hundredths, so 0.6 is more than 0.37.

6. The decimal point should not be in these signs. The way the prices are written, bananas cost less than a penny a pound, and the price of the paper is between one and two cents.

7. The Events Night held by Mr. Martinez's and Ms. Swanson's middle-school classes was a success, raising a total of *$645*. The teachers estimated the large turnout of middle-school students included over $\frac{3}{4}$ of the building's student population. Over half of the money, *$330.65*, was earned by the food booths. *215* game tickets were sold, raising *$161.25*, which represented $\frac{1}{4}$ of the money. The tickets were *75* cents each. Most of the money that was raised, *65%*, will go toward paying for the class camping trip, and the other *35%* will be used to pay expenses.

8. a. $\frac{8}{12} < \frac{3}{4}$ **b.** $\frac{5}{8} > \frac{6}{10}$ **c.** $\frac{2}{3} < \frac{5}{6}$

    d. $\frac{2}{4} < \frac{7}{12}$ **e.** $\frac{3}{8} > \frac{3}{12}$

9. Possible answer: Each space represents an eighth, because there are eight spaces between each number. Each mark would increase by an eighth: $\frac{1}{8}, \frac{2}{8}, \frac{3}{8}, \frac{4}{8}, \frac{5}{8}, \frac{6}{8}, \frac{7}{8}$. If the fractions are reduced, the marks are $\frac{1}{8}, \frac{1}{4}, \frac{3}{8}, \frac{1}{2}, \frac{5}{8}, \frac{3}{4}, \frac{7}{8}$.

10. a. $\frac{1}{4}$ **b.** $\frac{1}{2}$

11. $\frac{24}{15}, 1\frac{7}{10}, 1\frac{15}{18}$

12. The portion of the figure that is shaded is $\frac{10}{30}$ or $\frac{1}{3}$. If you divide the rectangle into 30 equal pieces, 10 of them are shaded, and $\frac{10}{30}$ equals $\frac{1}{3}$.

13. 3 worms; $3\left(\frac{2}{3}\right) = 2$. Students will probably draw a picture to show this, which is quite acceptable at this time.

14. a. True; possible explanation: If the denominators are the same, each piece is the same size. The fraction with the larger numerator is the larger fraction because numerators tell how many pieces you have.

b. False; possible explanation: If the numerators are the same, the number of pieces is the same. As the denominator increases, the size of the pieces decreases, so the fraction with the smaller denominator is the larger fraction.

15. a. Small slices are $\frac{1}{12}$ of a pizza, and large slices are $\frac{1}{8}$ of a pizza; $\frac{3}{12} + \frac{3}{8} = \frac{15}{24} = \frac{5}{8}$ of a pizza.

b. $1 - \frac{15}{24} = \frac{9}{24}$ of a pizza.

c. $\frac{2}{8} + \frac{9}{12} = 1; \frac{4}{8} + \frac{6}{12} = 1; \frac{6}{8} + \frac{3}{12} = 1$

16. Possible answers:

a.

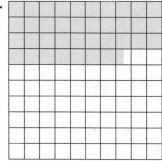

b.

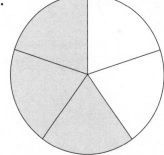

c.

Bits and Pieces I Assessment Answers *(continued)*

17. **a.** percent shaded: 12%; percent not shaded: 88%

    b. percent shaded: 8%; percent not shaded: 92%

    c. percent shaded: 30%; percent not shaded: 70%

18. 120 people; possible explanations: 20% means 20 out of every 100. You have 6 hundreds, so $6 \times 20 = 120$. 20% percent can be written as $\frac{1}{5}$, and a fifth of 600 is 120.

19. **a.** $\frac{375}{1,000}$ or $\frac{3}{8}$ **b.** $\frac{6}{10}$ or $\frac{3}{5}$ **c.** $\frac{5}{100}$ or $\frac{1}{20}$

20. **a.**

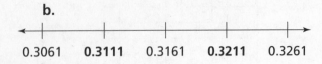

| 0.01 | **0.015** | **0.02** | **0.025** | 0.03 |

b.

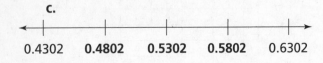

| 0.3061 | **0.3111** | 0.3161 | **0.3211** | 0.3261 |

c.

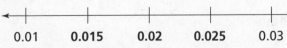

| 0.4302 | **0.4802** | **0.5302** | **0.5802** | 0.6302 |

21. **a.** $1\frac{1}{3}$ **b.** $2\frac{1}{2}$

22. **a.**

b.

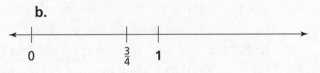

c.

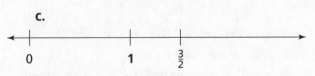

23. **a.** $\frac{3}{4}$ or 0.75   **b.** $\frac{4}{3}$ or $1.\overline{3}$

24. **a.** yes   **b.** no   **c.** yes

25. **a.** $1\frac{3}{5}$ slices   **b.** $\frac{4}{5}$ of an egg

Shapes and Designs Assessment Answers

Check-Up

1. This polygon has reflection symmetry. There are two lines of symmetry (one vertical and one horizontal). It also has rotation symmetry. It can be turned 180 degrees around its center point and will align back onto itself.

2. a. Answers will vary. Students could have used shape A (the equilateral triangle), B (the square), or D (the regular hexagon).

b. Answers will vary. Students could have used shape C (the pentagon), E (the heptagon), or F (the octagon).

3. a.

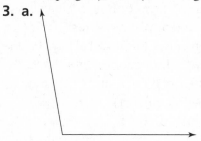

b. about 55°

4. 60°

Partner Quiz

1. a. Yes; squares can be used to tile since all angles are 90° and 4 × 90° = 360° which is the degree measure in a full turn.

b. No; regular pentagons cannot be used alone to tile a floor. Since the angle sum of a regular pentagon is 540°, each interior angle is 540° ÷ 5 = 108°, which is not a factor of 360°. Thus, copies of a 108° angle will not fit around a point.

2. a. Angle 1 = 90°; the symbol in the diagram indicates that it is a right angle.

b. Angle 5 = 40°; explanations will vary; some students may use an angle ruler to measure, and others may apply what they know about supplementary angles, alternate interior angles and the fact that the sum of the angles in a triangle is 180°.

c. Angle 6 = 50°; explanations will vary. The reasoning used for angle 5 also works with angle 6.

3. Yes, the parallelogram could have two angles with measures of 54° and two angles with measure 126° for an angle sum of exactly 360°.

4. Since the figure is a regular hexagon, the angle sum is 180° × 4 = 720° and thus each interior angle is 720° ÷ 6 = 120°. The triangle formed inside the hexagon has angles which are 120° and 30°. So, the third angle must be 30° since 120° + 30° + 30° = 180°.

Multiple-Choice Items

1. C	**2.** F	**3.** D	**4.** J
5. C	**6.** G	**7.** D	**8.** J

Unit Test

1. a.

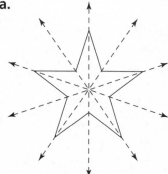

b. It also has five turn symmetries, specifically 72°, 144°, 216°, 288°, and 360°.

Note: It is not necessary for students to give the specific degrees of rotation symmetry.

Shapes and Designs Assessment Answers *(continued)*

2. **a.** The angle sum is $(5 - 2) \times 180° = 540°$. To find the angle sum, you can pick a vertex of the polygon and draw triangles. If you do this with a pentagon, you will get 3 triangles, each of which has 180°, so the answer is $3 \times 180° = 540°$.

   b. There are $360° \div 5 = 72°$ in each exterior angle. To find the number of degrees in the exterior angle of a regular polygon, you divide 360° by the number sides (or number of angles).

3. Ted's estimate is too large. The third side must have a length less than $7 + 3 = 10$.

4. No, the sum of the angles is $34° + 45° + 100° = 179°$. A triangle has an angle sum of exactly 180°.

5. Yes, you can make a rectangle with sides equal to 7, 7, 9, and 9 and then you can change the size of the opposite angles so the quadrilateral leans to make another quadrilateral with the same side lengths.

6. angle 1 = 90°, angle 2 = 60°, angle 3 = 30°, angle 4 = 135°, angle 5 = 45°.

7. 50°; since $ABCD$ is a rectangle all the angles are right angles, so the triangle formed by the diagonal is a right triangle. So $90° + 40° + x = 180°$ and thus x is 50°.

8. **a.** angle 1 = 40°, angle 2 = 75°, angle 3 = 105°, angle 4 = 140°.

   b. angle 5 = 140°, angle 6 = 105°.

Question Bank

1. **a.** Answers will vary. Students' measurements are typically between 75° and 90°.

   b. Answers will vary. Students' measurements are typically between 15° and 30°.

   c. Answers will vary. Students' measurements are typically between 105° and 120°.

   d. The angle for c is the largest. The angle for a is somewhat smaller. The angle for b is much smaller than the other two angles.

2. Marcelo is not right. You can make a quadrilateral with these four line segments since the sum of the three smallest sides $(3 + 6 + 6)$ is greater than the length of the longest side (12).

3. False; it could be a rectangle or it could be just a parallelogram. Thus the *always* part of the statement is not true.

4. False; it could be a parallelogram if the edges were put together in the order 7–11–7–11. But you could also put the edges together in the following order: 7–7–11–11 which would not give a parallelogram.

5. False; you can draw only one triangle of sides 3, 4, and 5. You can orient the figure in different ways, but it will always be a triangle with the same size and shape.

6. One possibility is (4, 3) and (7, 3); the other is (4, 9) and (7, 9).

7. Possible answer: (0, 5).
   Note: (5, 0) and (2, 5) will give right triangles and thus are incorrect. Make sure that two sides are greater than the third side in order for the figure to be a triangle.

8. Answers will vary.

9. Alejandro was correct. The sum of the angles that fit together around a point must be 360°. All the angles of a regular pentagon are 108° and multiples of 108 will not make 360.

10. Dallas to Boston, about 60° E; Boston to San Diego, about 105° W; San Diego to Detroit, about 75° E; Detroit to Miami, about 160° E

11. Answers will vary. Some students may measure with an angle ruler, and others may apply what they know about supplementary angles to find that angle 3 = 110°, and then use what they know about alternate interior angles to conclude that angle 1 = 110°.

Shapes and Designs Assessment Answers *(continued)*

12. True; three sides can form only one triangle. The triangle can be flipped or turned so that it looks slightly different because of its orientation, but it is still the same triangle.

13. False; it is possible to sequence the four line segments in more than one arrangement, such as 5-7-9-11, 5-9-7-11 or 5-9-11-7. Also, any quadrilateral can be "squished" into different-shaped quadrilaterals.

14. True; to be a parallelogram, a figure must have four sides, with opposite sides equal and opposite angles equal. A rectangle meets these requirements and has the additional requirement that all four of its angles are 90°.

15. False; not every parallelogram has four equal sides, or four right angles. However, a square is a special parallelogram.

16. True; the angles that fit around a single point must add to 360°. Because a square has 90° angles and the sum of four 90° angles is 360°, this will work.

17. False; the sum of the measures of the angles of any triangle is 180°.

18. False; in a regular hexagon, all angles are 120°.

19. True; because the sum of the angles in any triangle is 180°, the sum of the angles of two triangles is 360°, so six copies of the triangle will fit around a point with two copies of each angle around the point.

20. about 20°

21. about 80°

22. about 125°

23.

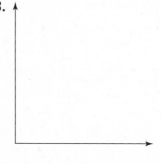

24.

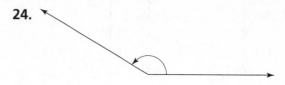

25. angle = 270°

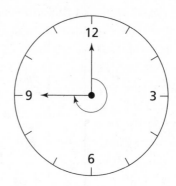

26. angle = 150°

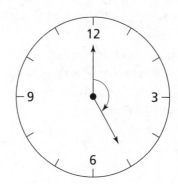

27. All sides are 2 cm and all angles are 90°.

28. Opposite sides must be of equal length, so the short side is 2 cm, the long side is 5 cm, and all the angles are 90°.

29. Opposite sides must be of equal length, so the short side is 2 cm, and the long side is 4 cm. Opposite angles must be equal, so the other obtuse angle is 120°. The two acute angles are equal, and each must be $\frac{360 - 240}{2} = 60°$.

30. Opposite sides must be of equal length, so the short side is 1 cm, and the long side is 3 cm. Opposite angles must be equal, so the other acute angle is 45°. The two obtuse angles are equal, and each must be $\frac{360 - 90}{2} = 135°$.

31. a. 45° **b.** 135°
  c. 180° **d.** 225°
  e. 270° **f.** 315°
  g. 0° **h.** 22.5°

32. a. The pentagon has five lines of symmetry, the lines connecting each vertex to the midpoint of the opposite side.

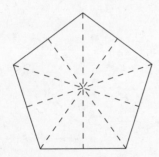

The regular pentagon also has five turn symmetries: 72°, 144°, 216°, 288°, and 360°.

  b. The rhombus has two lines of symmetry; the two diagonals of the shape. There are also two turn symmetries: 180° and 360°.

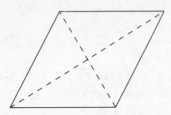

33. a. Jack's shape must be a square. Because its sides and angles are the same measure, the square is the only quadrilateral that can be turned 90° and fit back into the same spot.

  b. Kenesha's shape could be any quadrilateral other than a square. For example, students may choose a rectangle or a parallelogram and show how the adjacent angles, being different sizes, make it impossible to fit back into the original space.

34. a. No, because all sides and angles of the triangle are not equal.

  b. Yes; any triangle can be used to tile the plane.

35. Each side would have a length $\frac{12}{3} = 4$.

36. Each side would have length $\frac{16.4}{4} = 4.1$.

37. a. $x = 35°$ **b.** $x = 102°$ **c.** 43°

38. I, L, and V are all hexagons. X is not part of the group because, even though it has six line segments for sides, it is not a closed figure and therefore not a polygon.

39. E, G, H, I, and M are all regular polygons (all sides and all angles are equal). S is not part of the group because it is not a regular polygon. Only its sides are equal.

40. F, Q, W, and X are all grouped together because they are not polygons. These figures are either not closed (X) or do not have straight-line sides (F, Q, and W). N is closed and has straight-line sides and is therefore a polygon.

41. At first glance, it may appear that A, B, H, J, M, S, and U are grouped together because they are all quadrilaterals. Because N is also a quadrilateral means that one needs to look for something more specific. Thus A, B, H, J, M, S, and U are grouped because they are also all parallelograms. N is not part of the group because it is not a parallelogram.

Bits and Pieces II Assessment Answers

Check-Up

1. **a.** 1; Possible strategy: $\frac{2}{3}$ is a little more than $\frac{1}{2}$. If you add $\frac{1}{4}$ to a number that is a little more than $\frac{1}{2}$, you will have a little more than $\frac{3}{4}$, making the sum closest to 1.

   b. $\frac{1}{2}$; Possible explanation: $0.5 = \frac{3}{6}$ and so $\frac{3}{6} + \frac{1}{6} = \frac{4}{6}$ which is only $\frac{1}{6}$ away from $\frac{1}{2}$ and $\frac{2}{6}$ away from 1.

   c. 1; Possible explanation: $\frac{1}{8} + \frac{6}{8} = \frac{7}{8}$ which is one piece $\left(\frac{1}{8}\right)$ away from 1.

2. B; $\frac{5}{6}$ or about 0.83 added to 0.25 is equal to about 1.08 which is just slightly over 1. The other two are 0.25 or more over 1.

3. $\frac{8}{12}$ or $\frac{2}{3}$; $\frac{3}{12} + \frac{1}{12} + \frac{8}{12} = 1$ or $\frac{12}{12} - \frac{4}{12} = \frac{8}{12}$.

4. **a.** $2\frac{1}{2}$ pizzas: $\frac{8}{12} + \frac{7}{12} + \frac{5}{12} + \frac{10}{12} = \frac{30}{12}$ or $2\frac{1}{2}$.

   b. $\frac{1}{2}$ pizza; $3 - 2\frac{1}{2} = \frac{1}{2}$.

5. **a.** $\frac{22}{15}$ or $1\frac{7}{15}$; $\frac{10}{15} + \frac{12}{15} = \frac{22}{15}$.

   b. $11\frac{1}{24}$; $3\frac{16}{24} + 7\frac{9}{24} = 10\frac{25}{24}$ or $11\frac{1}{24}$.

   c. $\frac{7}{20}$; $\frac{15}{20} - \frac{8}{20} = \frac{7}{20}$.

   d. $1\frac{11}{12}$; $10\frac{8}{12} - 8\frac{9}{12} = 9\frac{20}{12} - 8\frac{9}{12} = 1\frac{11}{12}$.

Partner Quiz

1. $2\frac{1}{6}$ cups peanuts; Possible number sentence: $6\frac{1}{2} \times \frac{1}{3} = 2\frac{1}{6}$. $4\frac{7}{8}$ cups pretzels; Possible number sentence: $\frac{3}{4} \times 6\frac{1}{2} = 4\frac{7}{8}$. $1\frac{3}{10}$ cups raisins; Possible number sentence: $\frac{1}{5} \times 6\frac{1}{2} = 1\frac{3}{10}$. $4\frac{1}{3}$ cups popcorn; Possible number sentence: $\frac{2}{3} \times 6\frac{1}{2} = 4\frac{1}{3}$.

2. **a.** 30 miles; $2\frac{1}{2} \times 12 = 30$.

   b. 45 miles; $3\frac{3}{4} \times 12 = 36 + 9 = 45$.

3. **a.** $\frac{1}{2}$ pan; $\frac{2}{3} \times \frac{3}{4} = \frac{6}{12}$.

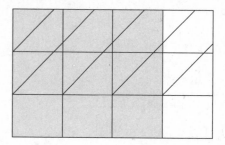

   b. $\frac{1}{2}$ pan; $\frac{2}{3} \times \frac{3}{4} = \frac{6}{12}$. It is different because each started with a different part of the whole pan.

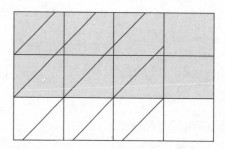

   c. Their friends ate the same amount of each pan.

4. There are many possibilities. Students may say something like:
   When I came home there were $1\frac{2}{3}$ pizzas in the refrigerator. I ate $\frac{1}{4}$ of what was left. How much did I eat?
   $1\frac{2}{3} \times \frac{1}{4} = 1 \times \frac{1}{4} + \frac{2}{3} \times \frac{1}{4} = \frac{1}{4} + \frac{2}{12} = \frac{5}{12}$ of a pizza
   OR
   $\frac{5}{3} \times \frac{1}{4} = \frac{5}{12}$ of a pizza

Multiple-Choice Items

1. C	**2.** H	**3.** D	**4.** G
5. B	**6.** F	**7.** D	**8.** H
9. A	**10.** H	**11.** B	**12.** H

Unit Test

1. a. $2\frac{1}{10}$ pages; $2 \times \frac{1}{5} + 9 \times \frac{1}{20} + 5 \times \frac{1}{4} = \frac{8}{20} + \frac{9}{20} + \frac{25}{20} = \frac{42}{20}$

b. $1\frac{1}{2}$; $3\frac{1}{5} - 1\frac{7}{10} = 2\frac{6}{5} - 1\frac{7}{10} = 2\frac{12}{10} - 1\frac{7}{10} = 1\frac{5}{10} = 1\frac{1}{2}$

2. a. $\frac{5}{8}$ pound on Monday

b. $1\frac{7}{8}$ pounds left over

c. $\frac{5}{8}$ pound on Tuesday

d. He ate the same on both days.

3. 30 smoothies; $3\frac{1}{3}$ divided by $\frac{1}{9} = \frac{10}{3} \cdot \frac{10}{3}$ divided by $\frac{1}{9} = \frac{30}{9} \cdot \frac{30}{9}$ divided by $\frac{1}{9} = 30$. OR $\frac{10}{3} \times \frac{9}{1} = \frac{90}{3} = 30$.

4. $3\frac{2}{3} \div \frac{1}{4} = \frac{11}{3} \times 4 = \frac{44}{3} = 14\frac{2}{3}$ bows

5. B; $\frac{11}{20} - \frac{4}{20} = \frac{7}{20}$

6. J; $\frac{2}{3}$ of 18 is 12, $\frac{1}{3}$ of 18 is 6 because 18 divided by 3 is 6.

7. C; $\frac{4}{20} + \frac{15}{20} = \frac{19}{20}$ and $\frac{4}{20} = \frac{1}{5}$

8. G; $\frac{18}{3}$ divided by $\frac{2}{3}$ is equal to 9 wholes.

9. $1\frac{1}{3} + \frac{5}{6} = \frac{4}{3} + \frac{5}{6} = \frac{8}{6} + \frac{5}{6} = \frac{13}{6}$ or $2\frac{1}{6}$

10. $1\frac{1}{3} - \frac{5}{6} = \frac{4}{3} - \frac{5}{6} = \frac{8}{6} - \frac{5}{6} = \frac{3}{6}$ or $\frac{1}{2}$

11. $1\frac{1}{3} \times \frac{5}{6} = \frac{4}{3} \times \frac{5}{6} = \frac{20}{18}$ or $1\frac{1}{9}$

12. $1\frac{1}{3} \div \frac{5}{6} = \frac{8}{6} \div \frac{5}{6} = 8 \div 5 = 1\frac{3}{5}$

Question Bank

1. a. The sum of $\frac{4}{5} + \frac{5}{8}$ is larger than the sum of $\frac{4}{7} + \frac{5}{9}$ because $\frac{4}{5}$ is larger than $\frac{4}{7}$ and $\frac{5}{8}$ is larger than $\frac{5}{9}$. Also, $\frac{4}{5} + \frac{5}{8} = \frac{57}{40} = 1\frac{17}{40}$ while $\frac{4}{7} + \frac{5}{9} = \frac{71}{63} = 1\frac{8}{63}$.

b. The difference $\frac{14}{12} - \frac{2}{8}$ is larger than the difference $\frac{10}{9} - \frac{2}{6}$ because $\frac{14}{12} - \frac{2}{8} = 1\frac{1}{6} - \frac{1}{4} = \frac{11}{12}$ or $\frac{33}{36}$ and $\frac{10}{9} - \frac{2}{6} = \frac{10}{9} - \frac{1}{3} = \frac{10}{9} - \frac{3}{9} = \frac{7}{9} = \frac{28}{36}$.

2. a. $15\frac{1}{4}$

b. No, he will be $4\frac{3}{4}$ hours short of working the hours he needs.

3. a. less than $\frac{2}{3}$ **b.** less than $\frac{2}{3}$

c. less than $\frac{2}{3}$ **d.** greater than $\frac{2}{3}$

4. Since the original recipe yields only 12 pancakes, you must multiply each ingredient by $\frac{30}{12} = \frac{5}{2} = 2\frac{1}{2}$ to mix a batch that would make 30.

$1\frac{1}{4} \times 2\frac{1}{2} = 3\frac{1}{8}$ cups flour

$1 \times 2\frac{1}{2} = 2\frac{1}{2}$ eggs

$3 \times 2\frac{1}{2} = 7\frac{1}{2}$ teaspoons baking powder

$1\frac{1}{2} \times 2\frac{1}{2} = 3\frac{3}{4}$ tablespoons sugar

$\frac{1}{2} \times 2\frac{1}{2} = 1\frac{1}{4}$ teaspoons salt

$\frac{3}{4} \times 2\frac{1}{2} = 1\frac{7}{8}$ cups milk

$2 \times 2\frac{1}{2} = 5$ tablespoons salad oil

5. a. At stage A, $\frac{1}{3}$ of the line is covered and $\frac{2}{3}$ of the line is not covered.

b. At stage B, $\frac{1}{3} + \frac{2}{9} = \frac{5}{9}$ of the line is covered and $\frac{4}{9}$ of the line is not covered.

c. At stage C, $\frac{5}{9} + \frac{4}{27} = \frac{19}{27}$ of the line is covered and $\frac{8}{27}$ of the line is not covered.

6. B

Covering and Surrounding Assessment Answers

Check-Up

1. Answers will vary. Possible answers:

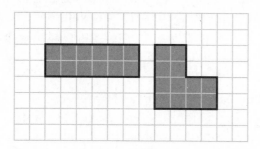

2. Area: 20 square centimeters, Perimeter: 18 cm; Possible explanation: I multiplied 5 by 4 to find the area. To find the perimeter I added the length and the width, then multiplied this answer by 2, in order to account for both lengths and both widths.

3. **a.** The problem does not specify to list the areas of each shelter. Nonetheless, they are included in the table below. Some students may list the 4 by 6 rectangle separately from the 6 by 4 rectangle, while some will list only one of these. Either way is acceptable.

Length	Width	Area
1	9	9
2	8	16
3	7	21
4	6	24
5	5	25

b. The 5 by 5 shelter has the largest area: 25 square feet.

c. The 1 by 9 shelter has the least area: 9 square feet.

d. The 5 by 5 shelter and the 4 by 6 shelter each hold 8 children under the code. The 5 by 5 shelter would have a little bit of extra space for these 8 children, but they would each hold the same number.

Partner Quiz

1. **a.** 18 square inches. (The mat is 30 square inches while the photo is 12 square inches.)

   b. 16 square inches. (The mat is 28 square inches while the photo is 12 square inches.)

   c. The rectangular mat will require 22 inches of frame materials. The non-rectangular mat will require 24 inches.

2. **a.** 34 centimeters. Students will need to measure the diagonal sides, which are each 5 cm.

   b. 42 square centimeters. Possible explanation: We cut the shape into a 5 by 6 rectangle and two triangles, each with base 4 cm and height 3 cm. The area of the figure is the sum of the areas of these smaller shapes: $6 + 6 + 30 = 42$.

3. **a.** False. These two parallelograms have the same side lengths, but their height is different, so their area is also different.

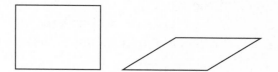

Covering and Surrounding Assessment Answers (continued)

b. True. Any two triangles with the same side lengths will be congruent. Congruent shapes have all measures (including area) the same.

Multiple-Choice Items

1. C   2. F   3. C
4. H   5. C   6. F
7. B
8. G, Students can reason this answer using triangle inequality learned in *Shapes and Designs*.
9. B

Unit Test

1. Area: 24 square inches, Perimeter: 22 inches
2. Area: 28 square centimeters, Perimeter: 32.3 centimeters
3. Area: 200.96 square centimeters, Perimeter/ Circumference: 50.24 centimeters
4. Area: 11 square centimeters, Perimeter: 22 centimeters
5. a. The 1 by 48 rectangle would have the largest perimeter: 98 units.
   b. The 6 by 8 rectangle would have the smallest perimeter: 28 units.
6. a. 113.04 square inches
   b. 40.82 square inches
   c. The square pizza has more area: 225 square inches against the round pizza's 200.96 square inches, for 24.04 more square inches.
   d. The crust of a pizza is measured by its perimeter or circumference. The square pizza has a larger perimeter (and therefore more crust), 60 inches against the 50.24 inches of crust on the round pizza.

7. a. The actual area, to the nearest square centimeters, is 110 square centimeters.
   b. Answers will vary but students should use the symmetry of the ellipse to be more efficient. Some students may use strategies similar to those they found for a circle. See the following note.

For the Teacher: Area of an Ellipse

The formula for the area of an ellipse is analogous to the formula for the area of a circle. For a circle, $A = \pi r^2$. In this unit, students think of this as being "a bit more than 3 radius squares."

An ellipse does not have a radius square. An ellipse has a major (long) and a minor (short) axis (below left). We can use half of each axis to create a rectangle (below right). Then the area of the ellipse is a little more than three times the area of this axis rectangle.

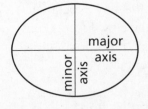 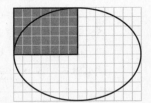

If we label the two half-axes a and b, then for an ellipse, $A = \pi ab$. It is **not** expected that students will come to this conclusion on the unit test. They are expected to apply techniques for estimation.

The case for circumference of an ellipse is much more complicated.

Covering and Surrounding Assessment Answers *(continued)*

Question Bank

1. a. area, square feet

b. area, square yards (or square feet)

c. perimeter, feet

d. The room is 3 yards (9 feet) by 4 yards (12 feet), so $3 \times 4 = 12$ square yards of carpet are needed (108 square feet is also correct).

e. $(9 + 12) \times 2 = 42$ feet of baseboard (Some students may argue for less than 42 feet—say, 39 feet—because of the door opening not needing baseboard. This is a reasonable answer as well.)

f. Possible answer: Two of the walls need $12 \times 8 = 96$ square feet of paint, two of the walls need $9 \times 8 = 72$ square feet of paint, and the ceiling needs $12 \times 9 = 108$ square feet of paint, so there is $(96 \times 2) + (72 \times 2) + 108 = 444$ square feet to cover. This would require $444 \div 350 \approx 1.27$ gallons of paint, so you would need $1\frac{1}{2}$ or 2 gallons (if the paint came only in full gallons).

2. a. Some students may know that the formula for the area of a trapezoid is $\frac{(b_1 + b_2)}{2} \times h$ and calculate $\frac{(3 + 5)}{2} \times 2 = 8$ square feet. Others may divide the trapezoid into a rectangle and two triangles, where the area of the rectangle is $3 \times 2 = 6$ square feet and the area of each congruent triangle is $2 \times 1 \div 2 = 1$ square foot for a total of $6 + 1 + 1 = 8$ square feet.

b. For two coats he needs to cover $8 \times 2 = 16$ square feet. A quart covers 32 square feet, and 16 is half of 32, so half a quart of paint is needed. If you can't buy the paint in half quarts, 1 quart would be needed.

3. a. area ≈ 39.3 square feet

b. For one coat she needs to cover 39.3 square feet. A quart covers 32 square feet, and $39.3 \div 32 \approx$

1.2 quarts. If the paint only comes in full quarts, 2 quarts would be needed. If you can buy the paint in half quarts, $1\frac{1}{2}$ quarts would be needed.

c. For a circle, the border would be $3.14 \times 10 = 31.4$ feet. For a semicircle, the border will be $31.4 \div 2 = 15.7$ feet

4. a. In small tile units, the area would be 48 square units and the perimeter would be 32 units.

b. Because it takes four small tiles to equal the area of one large tile, the area in small tile units is four times the area in large tile units. Because it takes two small tile edges to equal the length of one large tile edge, the perimeter in small tile units is twice the perimeter in large tile units.

5. a. The idea here is to find the pen with the largest area. If students use whole units, the pen with the largest area is a 10×11 rectangle. A more sophisticated answer would take into account the fact that whole units are not a restriction; thus the pen with the largest area would be a 10.5×10.5 square.

b. The idea here is to find the pen with the longest running area. The longest and thinnest design using whole-number units is a 20×1 rectangular pen. Some students might argue for the other sizes, such as a 19×2 pen, to give the dog more room to turn around.

c. If students use whole units, the pen could have fence side lengths of 10, 22, and 10 meters or 11, 20, and 11 meters which, with the house as the fourth side of the pen, results in an area of 220 square meters. A more sophisticated answer would involve considering rational numbers; the pen could have side lengths of 10.5, 21, and 10.5 meters and an area of 220.5 square meters.

d. Students might argue for a 3.5 × 35 meter pen because the house (which is 35 meters long) is to be one side on the pen and that leaves 7 meters for the two short ends. Others might argue that you could use the fencing to extend the house wall and suggest a 1.5 × 37 meter pen or a 1 × 37.5 meter pen.

6. a. yield sign: area = 3,000 square centimeters, so cost = $3.00
school zone sign: area = 7,921 square centimeters, so cost = $7.92
speed limit sign: area = 4,500 square centimeters, so cost = $4.50
railroad crossing sign: area = about 6,647.6 square centimeters, so cost = $6.65

b. yield sign: perimeter = 250 centimeters, so cost = $5.00
school zone sign: perimeter = 356 centimeters, so cost = $7.12
speed limit sign: perimeter = 270 centimeters, so cost = $5.40
railroad crossing sign: circumference = 288.9 centimeters, so cost = $5.78

7. a. The area of the floor is 28 × 20 = 560 square feet, so Lara need 560 floor tiles.

b. 560 × 0.75 = 420, so the tiles will cost $420.

c. The perimeter of the room is (28 + 20) × 2 = 96 feet, so Lara need 96 feet of baseboard.

d. Possible answer: Since 96 ÷ 16 = 6, Lara could buy six 16-foot lengths of baseboard.

e. The 10-foot lengths are a better buy, so Lara should buy as many of those as possible. She could buy eight 10-foot lengths and one 16-foot length (8 × 10 + 16 = 96).

f. Possible answers: Lara could buy four 10-foot boards (two for each of the shorter walls) and four 16-foot boards (two for each of the longer walls). Lara could buy six 16-foot boards, use two for each of the longer walls and use one 16-foot board plus the 4-foot length left over from the longer walls for each of the shorter walls. Each of these configurations would produce a seam at each corner and one on each wall.

g. Answers will vary: They should represent a reasonable tradeoff between price and number of seams.

Bits and Pieces III Assessment Answers

Check-Up 1

1. a. Estimate for $0.52 + 1.2$: a little less than $1\frac{3}{4}$ or 1.75. Possible explanation: I rounded 0.52 to $\frac{1}{2}$ and 1.2 to $1\frac{1}{4}$; $\frac{1}{2} + 1\frac{1}{4}$

Estimate for $4.4 - 1.29$: about $3\frac{1}{4}$ or 3.25. Possible explanation: I rounded 4.4 to $4\frac{1}{2}$ and 1.29 to $1\frac{1}{4}$; $4\frac{1}{2} - 1\frac{1}{4}$

b. 1.72 and 3.11

2. a. $1\frac{23}{100} + 3\frac{9}{10} = 1\frac{23}{100} + 3\frac{90}{100} = 4\frac{113}{100} = 5\frac{13}{100} = 5.13$

b. $2.4 + 3.07 = 5.47$

3. a. Dan had more by 18 cents. $1.02 - 0.84 = 0.18$

b. Dave got 8 cents more this week than Dan. Dave: $1.63 - 0.51 = 1.12$. Dan: $1.76 - .72 = 1.04$

c. $1.63 + 1.76 = 3.39$

Partner Quiz

1. $32.3 + 41.19 + 57.8 = 131.29$; $200.00 - 131.29 = 68.71$. She is under by 68.71 cm.

2. At $1.75 each event, a student can buy 8 tickets for $14 dollars. Attending 9 events would make the pass a better deal. $9 \times 1.75 = \$15.75$

3. Possible answers: $201 \times 0.15 = 30.15$, $2.01 \times 15 = 30.15$, $20.1 \times 1.5 = 30.15$.

Possible explanation for $201 \times 0.15 = 30.15$: Since one factor has a hundredths place and the other is a whole number, the product will be hundredths.

Possible explanation for $2.01 \times 15 = 30.15$: Since 2×15 is 30 you can use this information to place the decimal.

Possible explanation for $20.1 \times 1.5 = 30.15$: There is one decimal place in 20.1 and one decimal place in 1.5, the product needs to have two decimal places.

4. Possible answers: $1.11 \times 25 = 27.75$ and $111 \times 2.5 = 277.5$

Possible explanation: In the first problem there had to be a total of 2 decimal places in the two factors. In the second problem there had to be a total of 1 decimal place in the two factors.

Check-Up 2

1. a. The first sum is greater. $1.809 + 18.09 = 19.899$; $7.05 + 11.918 = 18.968$

b. They are equal. Both have answers of 4.507.

c. The first product is greater. $0.37 \times 7.5 = 2.775$; $25.13 \times 0.037 = 0.92981$

d. The second quotient is greater. $12.5 \div 0.25 = 50$ (can be thought of as $1250 \div 25$); $1.1 \div 0.02$ can be thought of as $110 \div 2 = 55$.

2. a. Answers will vary. Example: Jude bought some candies that cost $0.05 each. The bill came to $3.05 before tax. How many candies did she buy? (Or, students may write a problem for $305 \div 5$.)

b. The 3 is in the ones place. There are 3 ones.

c. The 5 is in the hundredths place. There are 5 hundredths.

d. $\frac{305}{100} \div \frac{5}{100} = \frac{305}{100} \times \frac{100}{5} = \frac{305}{5}$

   Think of this as $305 \div 5$, so the answer is 61.

e. The solution tells you there are 61 5's in 305. (Or there are 61 of 0.05 in 3.05.)

Multiple Choice Items

1. D	**2.** G	**3.** C	**4.** H
5. C	**6.** H	**7.** B	**8.** J
9. C	**10.** H	**11.** A	**12.** H

Unit Test

1. a. 44.377

   b. 5.178

   c. 51.66

   d. 46

2. a. Paul bought 61.001 gallons of gasoline.

   b. $91.50 or $91.51. ($1.50 × 61.001 gallons = $91.5015)

   c. 1358.3 miles (24809.4 − 23451.1)

3. No. If you bought a $100 item, the 30% discount would make the sale price $70. An additional 25% off of $70 is $17.50 making the sale price $52.50. Compare this to a $100 item that is 55% off. The cost would be $45.

4. a. $0.75. (0.05 × $14.90 = $0.745, so round it to $0.75)

   b. $2.24. (0.15 × $14.90 = 2.235, so round it to $2.24) Some students may triple the sales tax of $0.75, to get a 15% tip of $2.25.

   c. Food plus tax plus tip is $17.89. Divide by 3, and you get $5.963333… So, round the amount up to $5.97 for all three people in the group to pay.

5. a. $13.91; 1.29 + 5.99 + 3.49 + 2.35 = 13.12. With 6% tax, the total will be $13.12 + $0.79 = $13.91.

   b. Yes; $13.91 + $5.39 = $19.30 or if you over-estimate $14 + 5.50 = 19.50. With 20 you will have enough money.

6. No. Each factor is a decimal to the hundredths place meaning the solution will be to the thousandths place (100 × 100). The solution should be 0.4761.

7. 12.4 − 3.2 = 9.2; 12.4 − 9.2 = 3.2; 3.2 + 9.2 = 12.4; 9.2 + 3.2 = 12.4; 3.2 × 4.1 = 13.12; 4.1 × 3.2 = 13.12; 13.12 ÷ 4.1 = 3.2; 13.12 ÷ 3.2 = 4.1

8. a. 3 × 1.08 = 3.24 pounds

   b. 3 pounds

Question Bank

1. **a.** Answers will vary based on your local sales tax. The cost before tax is $2 \times 7.98 + 2 \times 6.35 + 2 \times \frac{1}{2} \times 6.35 + 3 \times 1.98 + 19.99 = \$60.94$. At a 6% tax rate, the cost would be $64.60.
    b. Troy had enough money. At a 6% tax rate, he had $35.40 extra.

2. In the first lunch period, there are $0.3 \times 150 = 45$ students. In the second lunch period, there are $0.2 \times 150 = 30$ students. This leaves 50% (or half) for the third lunch period, or 75 students.

3. $\frac{16}{48} = 0.3333$, or $33\frac{1}{3}$%

4. Using the coupon, Ted would save $\frac{0.50}{1.59} \approx 0.3144$, or about 31.4%.

5. The tip can be figured in two ways, before tax and after tax.
    Evaluating the tip on the food cost before tax: The tip is $14.90 \times 0.15 = \$2.235$ or $2.24. The tax is $14.90 \times 0.05 = \$0.745$ or $0.75. The total bill is $14.90 + \$0.75 + \$2.24 = \$17.89$. Each person should pay about $17.89 \div 3 = \$5.97$
    Evaluating the tip on the food cost after tax: The tax is $14.90 \times 0.05 = \$0.745$ or $0.75. The check total is $14.90 + \$0.75 = \$15.65$. The tip is $15.65 \times 0.15 = \$2.3475$ or $2.35. The total bill is $15.65 + \$2.35 = \$18.00$. Each person should pay about $18.00 \div 3 = \$6.00$

6. **a.** Coat at store 1: $84 - \frac{1}{3} \times 84 = \$56$
    Coat at store 2: $76 - \frac{1}{4} \times 76 = \$57$
    The coat at store 1 is the better buy.
    b. To calculate the catalog price takes several steps:
    Step 1: Find the price after discount: $84 - 0.3 \times \$84 = \$58.80$
    Step 2: Apply the coupon: $58.80 - \$5.00 = \$53.80$
    Step 3: Add the shipping charge: $53.80 + 0.06 \times \$53.80 = \$57.03$
    Therefore the coat at the store is a better buy.

7. Answers will vary based on your local sales tax. For example, if your local sales tax is 6%, the product would have to cost $10.50.

8. The cost of renting a drum set for one year is $25 + (12 \times \$39.95) = \$504.40$.

9. **a.** 328.689
    b. 0.193
    c. 37.632
    d. 3.2

10. **a.** $0.625 + 1.5 = 2.125$
    b. $2.75 - 1.125 = 1.625$
    c. $4.125 \times 2.5 = 10.3125$
    d. $3.75 \div 1.25 = 3$

11. 1,080 miles

12. $10.375 - 5.25 = 5.125$ pounds

13. 12 boys

14. C

How Likely Is It? Assessment Answers

Check-Up

1. **a.** Yes. Each time Rachel tosses the coin, it has a 50% possibility of landing heads up.

   b. It is not very likely that a coin will land the same way ten times in a row. There are many ways a coin can land in ten tosses; ten heads is only one possibility.

For the Teacher

The number of different results of tossing a fair coin 10 times is 1,024 or 2^{10}. For example, TTTTTTTTTH or TTTTTTTTHT. Therefore, the probability of getting 10 heads is exactly $\frac{1}{1,024}$.

   c. Statement **iii** is true, because the coin is fair. Every time she tosses the coin, the probability of landing heads up is exactly 50%.

2. $\frac{5}{8}$. Either the event will happen or it won't—in other words, the probability that the event will happen plus the probability that the event will not happen is 1.

3. Possible answers: Drawing a blue block from a bag with 3 red blocks, 1 blue block, and 1 yellow block and drawing a red block from that same bag are not equally likely since P(red) = $\frac{3}{5}$ and P(blue) = $\frac{1}{5}$. Rolling a prime number on a standard die and rolling a 2 are not equally likely since P(prime) = $\frac{3}{6}$ and P(2) = $\frac{1}{6}$.

4. $\frac{5}{4}$ cannot be a probability because probabilities are always less than or equal to 1.

5. **a.** The experimental probability is 0, since it never happened. The theoretical probability is $\frac{1}{6}$.

   b. The experimental probability is $\frac{6}{20}$, but the theoretical probability is $\frac{1}{6}$.

   c. With so many possible outcomes, Mandy did not do enough trials to get a good estimate for the theoretical probability from an experiment.

6. **a.** Possible answers: Pulling a red block out of a bag containing only red blocks; flipping a coin and getting either heads or tails.

   b. Possible answer: Pulling a black block out of a bag containing only red blocks.

   c. 0

Partner Quiz

1. The game is indeed fair as long as the chips are fair. The probability that each player will get a point in each turn is equal. Since one chip will always be X, only the XY chip affects the game.

2. Answers will vary. The answers may be close to even, but will probably not be exactly ten matches and ten non-matches. Most pairs will probably obtain results suggesting that the game is fair. Give credit for good reasoning in this problem.

3. The class results will most likely suggest that the game is fair. Students should not argue that the game is unfair because the numbers of matches and non-matches are not exactly even. Make sure they understand experimental probability.

4. The class data are a better indicator of the experimental probability than the individual data because the class data includes more trials. The more trials, the better predictor the data of what is likely to happen.

Multiple Choice Items
1. C **2.** J **3.** C **4.** G
5. D **6.** F **7.** D

Unit Test
1. Answers will vary. Most students will get results suggesting that the game is unfair.

2. a. Answers will vary depending on class results.
b. Answers will vary depending on class results.
c. The class results will probably indicate that the game is unfair, getting closer to theoretical probability of $\frac{6}{8}$ or $\frac{3}{4}$ that two chips will match.

3. a. The theoretical probability that two chips will match is $\frac{6}{8} = \frac{3}{4}$. There are 8 possible outcomes (XXY, XXZ, XZY, XZZ, YXY, YXZ, YZY, YZZ) and 6 where two chips match.
b. The theoretical probability that no chips will match is $\frac{2}{8} = \frac{1}{4}$.
c. Answers will vary, but the class results most likely will be close to the theoretical results.

d. No, the Toss 3 Chips game is not fair. Theoretically, tossing two chips that match and tossing three different parts is not equally likely.

4. a. $P(\text{blue}) = \frac{4}{12} = \frac{1}{3}$
b. $P(\text{blue}) = \frac{8}{24} = \frac{1}{3}$
c. They are the same because doubling the amount of each marble color does not change the part to whole relationship. In both situations there is 1 blue for every three marbles.
d. Add 4 blue marbles. In the original bag, $P(\text{blue}) = \frac{4}{12}$. If you add 4 blue marbles, $P(\text{blue}) = \frac{8}{16}$ or $\frac{1}{2}$.

5. a. $P(\text{purple}) = \frac{1}{12}$. $P(\text{purple}) = 1 - [P(\text{orange}) + P(\text{yellow})] = 1 - \left(\frac{3}{4} + \frac{1}{6}\right) = 1 - \left(\frac{9}{12} + \frac{2}{12}\right) = 1 - \frac{11}{12} = \frac{1}{12}$.
b. Number of Purple: $\frac{1}{12} \times 36 = 3$; Number of Yellow $\frac{1}{6} \times 36 = 6$; Number of Orange: $\frac{3}{4} \times 36 = 27$

6. a. No, they are not equally likely.
$P(1) = \frac{1}{12} + \frac{1}{12} + \frac{1}{12} = \frac{3}{12}$ or $\frac{1}{4}$
$P(2) = \frac{1}{4} + \frac{1}{12} + \frac{1}{12} = \frac{3}{12} + \frac{2}{12} = \frac{5}{12}$
$P(3) = \frac{1}{4} + \frac{1}{12} = \frac{3}{12} + \frac{1}{12} = \frac{4}{12}$ or $\frac{1}{3}$
b. 50 times. If spun 120 times, you would expect to land on two $\frac{5}{12} \times 120$ or 50 times.

Question Bank

1. Answers will vary.

   For the Teacher: Extending Question Bank Question 1

   You could assign this question as a miniproject. Students could exchange and evaluate each other's games.

2. Answers will vary. This unit has not addressed the mathematics students need to analyze this problem theoretically, but they should be able to simulate it. For example, students could use four different-colored but otherwise identical items, draw them from a container one at a time (replacing after each draw), and count how many times they must do this until they have drawn all four colors. Or, students could divide a spinner into four equal sections, label each section for the four action figures, and count the spins it takes to get one of each figure. Students would need to repeat their experiment until they had enough data to make a reasonable prediction. From their experiences in this unit, they should communicate their understanding that a large number of trials will result in an experimental probability that is a good predictor. Ten trials are too few to count on the results being dependable, and more than 50 is probably too many to expect students to do. The data for ten trials might look like this: 6, 10, 4, 14, 9, 12, 8, 5, 13, 6, which gives an average of 8.7 (or 9) boxes of cereal needed to collect all four figures.

3. **a.** $\frac{2}{8} = \frac{1}{4}$; There are eight possible outcomes, all equally likely: HHH, HHT, HTH, HTT, THH, THT, TTH, and TTT. Only two outcomes (TTT and HHH) have all three coins matching.

   b. $\frac{4}{8} = \frac{1}{2}$; Four of the eight outcomes (HHH, HHT, HTH, and THH) include at least two heads.

4. Answers will vary.

5. **a.** There are 16 different ways to answer the questions.

Question 1	Question 2	Question 3	Question 4
T	T	T	T
T	T	T	F
T	T	F	T
T	T	F	F
T	F	T	T
T	F	T	F
T	F	F	T
T	F	F	F
F	T	T	T
F	T	T	F
F	T	F	T
F	T	F	F
F	F	T	T
F	F	T	F
F	F	F	T
F	F	F	F

   b. P(4 right) $= \frac{1}{16}$

   c. P(at least 2 right) $= \frac{11}{16}$

   Note to teacher: Check that students are not thinking about P (4 "true"), which is not the same question as P (4 "correct"), though the probabilities are the same.

6. a. The recommendations in the magazines are based on a very large sample; the friends' recommendations are based on a very small sample.

b. If students argue to follow their friends' recommendations, they are being persuaded by factors such as the desire to be like one's friends and are missing the idea that predictions are best made by considering a large number of trials.

7. a. June 3 and June 8 results are furthest from the expected 15 heads.

b. Students might make a bar graph to show how the percentages change. They may need help setting up the graph.

Day	Number of Heads	Accumulated Percent Heads
June 1	14	$\frac{14}{30}$ 46.66%
June 2	11	$\frac{25}{60}$ 41.66%
June 3	20	$\frac{45}{90}$ 50%
June 4	16	$\frac{61}{120}$ 51%
June 5	19	$\frac{80}{150}$ 53%
June 6	16	$\frac{96}{180}$ 53%
June 7	11	$\frac{107}{210}$ 51%
June 8	10	$\frac{117}{240}$ 49%
June 9	16	$\frac{133}{270}$ 49%
June 10	18	$\frac{151}{300}$ 50%

8. a. Two possible suggestions: Make a spinner that is divided equally into four sections each of which represents a different animal. Roll a die. If a one comes up they get a rabbit, if a 2 is rolled they get a hamster, a three they get an iguana and a 4 they get a tarantula.

b. Possible suggestion for if a student picks *rabbit*. Pick blocks from a bag containing 2 red (corresponding to *rabbit*), 1 white (hamster), 1 blue (iguana) and 1green (tarantula). There is a greater chance for the rabbit to be chosen since $P(\text{red}) = \frac{2}{5}$ and all the other animal probabilities are $\frac{1}{5}$.

9. a. Make a list of all possible outcomes and find the theoretical probabilities. This would show that HH $\left(\frac{1}{4}\right)$ or TT $\left(\frac{1}{4}\right)$ can occur only once while HT or TH can occur twice $\left(\frac{1}{2}\right)$.

b. Tell her that we need to play more rounds to see the patterns that emerge over the long run.

10.

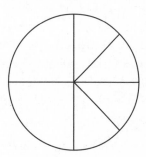

Each section is 60° or $\frac{1}{6}$ of the circle.

11. Possible answer:

The two large sections are $\frac{1}{4}$ of the circle.

The four small sections are $\frac{1}{8}$ of the circle.

12. Statement **c.** is true. When tossing two coins, there are four possible outcomes: HH, HT, TH, and TT. Thus, the probability of getting a match is $\frac{2}{4}$, or 50%, and the probability of not getting a match is $\frac{2}{4}$, or 50%.

13. 7; There are 36 possible combinations of a roll of two number cubes. Six of the 36 combinations give a sum of 7; $P(\text{sum of } 7) = \frac{6}{36} = \frac{1}{6}$. The next closest are the sums of 6 and 8, with five combinations each; $P(\text{sum of } 6) = P(\text{sum of } 8) = \frac{5}{36}$.

14. $\frac{7}{16}$

15. **a.** $\frac{3}{8}$ **b.** $\frac{5}{8}$

16. **a.** $\frac{32}{50} = \frac{16}{25}$

b. $\frac{32}{50} + \frac{7}{50} + \frac{1}{50} = \frac{40}{50} = \frac{4}{5}$

c. 77, because $\frac{7}{50} = \frac{77}{550}$

17.

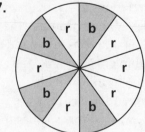

About $\frac{2}{5}$ should be blue and $\frac{3}{5}$ should be red.

18. $\frac{5}{4}$; All probabilities are numbers from 0 to 1. Since $\frac{5}{4}$ is greater than 1, it cannot be a probability.

Data About Us Assessment Answers

Check-Up

1. a. There are 25 people represented. The mode is 7. The median is 6. The range is from 3 letters to 9 letters

b. There are 36 people represented. The mode is November. The median and range are not appropriate representations for categorical data.

2. Students need to place at least one X over the 6 and one X over the 16. The remaining nine pieces of data must be distributed so that the median has a value of 12. Possible answers: (Figures 1 and 2)

3. a. Possible answers: How many books do you read in a month? How many books do you buy in a year? How many days should the book fair run? What is the most you are willing to pay for a paperback book? This data might be useful to the media specialist in deciding how many books to bring.

b. Possible answers: What is your favorite subject for reading? Who is your favorite author? What should we sell at the book fair in addition to books? This data might be useful to the media specialist in deciding how many books to bring.

Partner Quiz

1. a. 3 students

b. 3 students

c. The cuff will be tight.

d. The cuff will be loose.

2. a. (This data could also be expressed as a back-to-back stem plot.)

Grade 5 Data

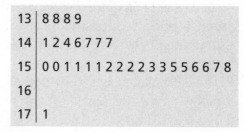

```
13 | 8 8 8 9
14 | 1 2 4 6 7 7 7
15 | 0 0 1 1 1 1 2 2 2 2 3 3 5 5 6 6 7 8
16 |
17 | 1
```

Grade 8 Data

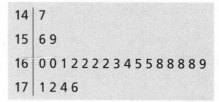

```
14 | 7
15 | 6 9
16 | 0 0 1 2 2 2 2 3 4 5 5 8 8 8 8 9
17 | 1 2 4 6
```

b. Answers should fall around 150 cm. Students may use one or more of these measures to justify their answer: median: 151; modes: 151, 152; range: 138–171

Figure 1

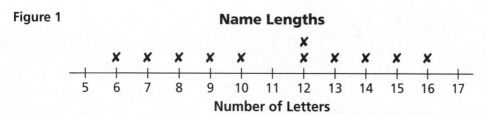

Name Lengths

Number of Letters

Figure 2

Name Lengths

Number of Letters

c. Answers should fall around 164 centimeters. Students may use one or more of these measures to justify their answer: median: 164; modes: 162, 168; mean: 164.43; range: 147–176

d. The data seem to cluster around one 10-centimeter range. In grade 5, it is the 150's; in grade 8, it is the 160's. There is an outlier on the tall end in grade 5 and somewhat of an outlier on the short end in grade 8. The distribution seems to shift up 10 centimeters from grade 5 to grade 8.

e. The median increases to 164.5; the modes remain the same.

Multiple Choice Items

1. B   **2.** G   **3.** C
4. J   **5.** D   **6.** G

Unit Test

1. a. 2
   b. 3

c. The mean increases (to about 3.6 children per family) because the total number of children increased while the number of families did not change.

2. Possible answers: group 1: 3, 1, 1, 2, 8; group 2: 5, 2, 2, 3, 3

3. a. 5–99
   b. 73; Only one student had that score.

4. a. 22 paces
   b. The line plot and the bar graph show representations of the same data. The bar graph requires a vertical scale to read the numbers of data in each group, while the numbers on the line plot can be found by counting the X's in each column. (Figure 3)
   c. The student who traveled the distance in 25 paces has the shorter pace. It took that student more paces to travel the same distance as the student who traveled the distance in only 17 paces.

Figure 3

Paces to the Gym

A bar graph titled "Paces to the Gym" with the vertical axis labeled "Number of Students" (0 to 7) and the horizontal axis labeled "Number of Paces" (17 to 25). The bars show: 17: 2, 18: 1, 19: 3, 20: 2, 21: 2, 22: 7, 23: 5, 24: 3, 25: 2.

Data About Us Assessment Answers *(continued)*

Question Bank

1. There are 10 people represented. The mode is 4. The median is 5. The range is 4–7.

2. Possible answers:

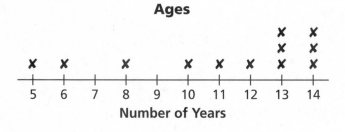

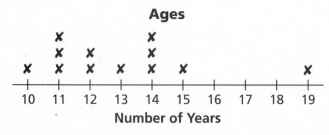

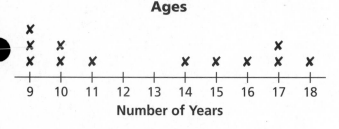

3. a. 30 children

   b. Possible answer: 4, 4, 5, 5, 6, 6

   c. No, they would not have to be the same. Other sets could be, for example, 2, 4, 5, 5, 6, 8 and 1, 4, 5, 5, 6, 9.

4. You are dividing the total number of children among many families. If each family has two children and there are some children left over, they must be divided equally among all the families. Since you are dealing with the distribution of numbers, this comes up mathematically as a fraction of a number. The mean of the distribution would be a whole number only if the number of families were a factor of the number of children.

5. a. Answers will vary. The statistic was probably determined by recording how far a sample group of people recorded walked in a day. The mean distance was calculated from the sample. This was multiplied by the number of days in a year, and the result was multiplied by the life expectancy of people today.

   b. Possible answer: I would have people wear a pedometer for a week and keep daily records. I would then scale this to meet my population's life expectancy.

6. a. yes; If there were more students without pets than students with pets, the median would be 0.

   b. yes; If no students had pets, the mean would be 0.

7. A   **8.** H   **9.** B   **10.** J

11. B   **12.** H   **13.** C